RECOVERY:
AN ALIEN CONCEPT?

RON COLEMAN

Edited by Eleanor Longden

P&P
PRESS LTD

© Ron Coleman 2011

First published in the United Kingdom in 1999 by
Handsell Publications

2nd Edition 2003 by P & P Press, Fife

3rd Edition 2011 by P & P Press
28 Habost, Port of Ness, Isle of Lewis, HS2 0TG,
Tel: +44 (0)1851 810060
Email: info@workingtorecovery.co.uk
www.workingtorecovery.co.uk

ISBN: 978-0-956304-82-7

Cover design: The Puffin Room
Typesetting: Two Ravens Press
www.tworavenspress.com

Dedication

To all those who have died before recovery became a reality: if there is an afterlife, may you find recovery and healing there. To all those who still await recovery: it is yours for the taking.

In Memory
Ron Coleman Senior
RIP

Contents

Acknowledgements

This is the part of any book that no author likes writing, for within this section there is a great danger of missing someone out. If I have forgotten to name you here, then accept my apologies now – but here goes:

Special mention must go to my partner Karen and the kids Victoria, Liam, Alex, John, Finn, Rory and Francesca, who put up with my swinging moods as I rewrote this book.

Special thanks also to Ian Parker for the critique on self and ownership that forced me to think through the chapter on the four selves.

Dr Terrence McLaughlin, who has sadly died: without him this book would never have seen the light of day. With him I had many debates and discussions that have shaped much of my thinking.

Marius Romme and Sandra Escher, as always, have been my inspiration in writing this book. They more than any others have guided my thinking, and I can never thank them enough. Indeed, when I thought the draft of this edition was ready for the printer I sent it to Marius Romme for comments, which ultimately resulted in a great deal more writing. He is responsible for many of the changes in the layout and the expansion of the content.

John Jenkins is also instrumental in the writing of this book, for he allowed me to develop my beliefs around recovery in practice. Thanks also to Alison Reeves, who wrote the booklet *Recovery: A Holistic Approach* (Reeves, 1997). Her work made me stop and think about the importance of recovery. She is still a special friend.

The biggest surprise for me in preparing a third edition

has been re-formatting the book in order to make it an easier read. This has included, for the first time, a bibliography and index, forced on me by pressure from my mentor Marius Romme. I have also had assistance from Eleanor Longden in formatting and editing (again a new experience for me) and I owe Eleanor a great deal of thanks for this, as for the first time the book will be ordered in a way that will make sense to more than just me. I have also indulged myself by looking at how systems and practice might come together to create a whole systems approach. I would like to put on record once again the help that John Jenkins has given me in thinking through this section.

Last and not least, I want to thank Mike Smith who has also contributed in many ways to this book. When Mike and I first met, I do not think either of us realised what we were to spark off in each other. We are now close friends and still work together regularly. Together we hold a dream that one day recovery will become the norm in mental health, and Mike continues to work tirelessly towards this goal.

Finally, to all those I have not mentioned above, especially Ian Murray (RIP); he is still an inspiration. Thank you very much; you know who you are.

Introduction to the
Third Edition

Mental illness, madness, or whatever you choose to call it, has been a preoccupation of mine from the first day that I walked – or rather was dragged – into the Royal Free psychiatric unit in London. That was the day that a psychiatrist who had known me for less than one hour concluded that I was suffering from a mental illness called schizophrenia. This one-hour meeting changed my whole life. Admittedly my life up to this point had not been the most enjoyable life on record. Indeed, it had been a fairly lonely and unhappy existence. A few months as an in-patient changed all that. Far from being lonely and unhappy, I became totally isolated and depressed. For the next ten years my life was to be controlled by the psychiatric system. In that time my brother-in-law, on meeting me for the first time, thought: 'What the hell is that?' He was referring to the pitiful sight that I had become when he met me five years after my admission into hospital. He later told me he wanted to shoot me to put me out of my misery.

Far from being a sanctuary and a system of healing, the psychiatric system became for me, like for so many others, a system of fear and continuation of illness. Like so many others, recovery was a process that I did not encounter within the system. Indeed, I can honestly say that it was not until I left the system that the recovery process really got underway in my life.

It was as if the system had no expectation of me recovering; instead the emphasis was on maintenance. I am not saying that those who worked in the system did not care for me. They did: they clothed me, fed me, housed me, and ensured that I took my medication. What they did not do was consider the possibility that I could return to being a person. Not as I once was, but the person that I could become; perhaps even more than I once was. Indeed, I could become Ron Coleman.

Within the pages of this book I hope to explore with you the possibility that recovery can be a reality: not just for the lucky one or two, but a real option for every person who enters the psychiatric system. In this new millennium there is a need to reflect on the past and to learn the lessons of history. *Recovery: An Alien Concept?* is an attempt to do just this. It is not an academic book, I hope, though students may find it useful. Rather it is an exploration of recovery, hopefully a guidebook, and perhaps a book that will encourage professionals, clients, and carers to begin their own personal journeys towards recovery.

This is the third edition of *Recovery: An Alien Concept?* and it is my intention to make this edition the final edition. The main reason I am amending the book is to bring it up to date with my own thinking about recovery, both as a theory and as a practice. This edition contains new chapters as well as revisions of the original material.

In Chapter One I describe my own journey into madness, the life events that precipitated it, and the response meted out to me by the psychiatric system. In contrast, Chapter Two outlines my personal 'stepping stones' to recovery, including individuals who helped steer and guide my recovery process, and the importance of self and ownership in reclaiming one's life. In Chapter Three I explore current definitions of recovery, particularly the dominant constructs clinical and social, and discuss some of the inherent limitations in these descriptions. Chapter Four provides an alternative viewpoint, in which I examine the reclamation of personal power within recovery, including ideas on deconstructing the power of the psychiatric system and reconstructing power as a personal commodity. Chapter Five discusses the role professionals have to play as agents of recovery, both as individuals and as part of a team approach, and Chapter Six develops these ideas by exploring how the diversity of the recovery experience can be promoted more effectively within the statutory sector. In Chapter Seven, I provide practical guidance by considering the role person-centred planning has to play in ensuring that a person's journey through the mental health system has an end as well as a beginning. Finally, Chapter Eight contains some of my reflections about the current crisis facing the psychiatric system, and suggestions for embracing not just the theory and concept, but the practice and reality of recovery.

I hope that those who read this book will find in its pages not only criticism of the present system, and the pain of those whom the system has failed, but also hope for the future, the inspiration of those who have recovered, and finally a desire to make recovery a reality in this now decade-old millennium.

Ron Coleman
Isle of Lewis, Scotland, 2011

Chapter One

THE MAKING OF A SCHIZOPHRENIC

There is a joke that many service users know that goes like this: *What is the difference between God and a psychiatrist? Answer: God does not think he is a psychiatrist.*

There is another major difference between God and a psychiatrist. Whereas it took God six days to create the world, a psychiatrist can change a person's world in a little under an hour. If the journey to recovery is a difficult one for many, it is often the case that the journey to illness is far too easy. My own journey to illness, far from being a series of biological or chemical events, was in simple words the culmination of personal life events that I had never dealt with.

Before I tell my story, I would like to point out that it is not that much different from the millions of others worldwide who have been in, or are still in, the psychiatric system. I am no braver or cleverer than most others in the system, neither am I somehow different. My story is an ordinary one, and should be treated as such.

Those of you who read the introduction to this book will know that a doctor in London diagnosed me as having schizophrenia. If you did not know this, then you have not read the introduction and should do so now. But my story does not start with an enforced meeting with a psychiatrist in 1982: it starts a long time before this. It starts, in fact, in 1969 with a young boy's desire to become a Roman Catholic priest. I was that young boy, and though people laugh now when I tell them I wanted to be a priest, at the age of eleven

1

I was smitten by the thought.

I was brought up in a working-class, Scottish-Irish Roman Catholic family, and like many boys my age I went through my religious phase in my eleventh year of life. I went to see our parish priest and told him that I wanted to join the priesthood. At this time he was getting on in years and was one of the old school, having said more masses in Latin than in English. He was also without doubt a man of God who saw himself as a shepherd, and we mere mortals as his flock. When one amongst his flock stated that they wanted to become a priest, he took them seriously. He took my desire to become a priest seriously, and once a week I met with him and two other boys who had also stated a desire to enter the priesthood. In these weekly meetings we would discuss the teachings of the church, the role of the priest, and whether we thought our calling to the priesthood was real. After one such discussion one of the boys stopped coming, as he felt he was not being called but was trying to please his family. The two of us that remained were undeterred and continued on with our instruction, fully committed to the idea that some day we would become priests.

These were happy days for me. I was preparing to serve God, and I had all the enthusiasm an eleven-year-old could muster for my coming tasks. The day that changed my life started the same as any other. I went to school and afterwards I headed to the chapel house for instruction. The housekeeper answered the door; she was near to tears as she told me our parish priest had been taken seriously ill earlier in the day. He survived this illness, but he never returned to our parish. (I often wonder what would have happened had he never become ill. Would I now be a priest?) Shortly after this happened, a new priest arrived (I will call him Adrian).

At first everything was business as usual, and I soon relaxed into my normal routine. The next three months went by without incident as far as I was concerned, though I noticed that a lot of the altar boys were leaving service before they normally would.

I was very quickly to discover the reason why, when after Mass one day Father Adrian asked me to come and see him in the vestry. I sauntered over without any thought as to why he wanted to see me; after all, he was a priest. When I arrived, Father Adrian asked me to sit down. It was at this point that things started to change. He began by asking me if I had any sins that I needed to confess. When I said I did not, he called me a liar and said that he needed to pray for me so that I would be forgiven. He knelt beside me and started praying aloud; he was saying something about me leading him into sin, and that I was evil. As he continued to pray he started moaning and groaning. I was aware that his hand was slowly moving up my leg; this went on until he was touching my penis. As this continued, I was aware of becoming a spectator to what was happening to me. I became conscious of other things around me, like the candles that were burning too brightly, and his purple vestments that were, if anything, even more purple than usual. I was there, but not there. Those who have been abused will know what I mean. Much later in my life, I discovered that this is called dissociation, and it is the most common form of self-preservation for those who are abused. But at the time it did not feel like much of a defence to me, for inside I screamed at him to stop. I also screamed at God for protection, but either God was deaf or I never screamed loud enough, because he never defended me. When it was over, Adrian told me that no one would believe me if I disclosed what had happened. I left the vestry

3

in a daze and never told anyone what had occurred that day, or the many other days that it was to continue for.

I was trapped for a while within this cycle of abuse; after all, who would believe me? Adrian was a priest: he stood between people and God, he represented Christ on earth, the forgiver of sins, the good shepherd. I was an eleven-year-old boy, a dreamer, and to say anything would brand me a liar. My relationship with this God that I thought I believed in was over. The abuse continued for a few months until I found from somewhere the strength to turn my back fully on the church, and with it God. My spiritual and religious phase was over. Time has taught me that this is the pattern with abusers; that they are often in positions of trust in the community, and that they use this position to ply their evil trade in misery and pain. Experience has taught me that the failure to deal with abuse means that the abuse will stay with you throughout your life, and in many ways shape your life in terms of future relationships. This is especially true when it comes to trusting friends or life partners. This event, more than any other, was to shape my life; or should I say 'illness'.

If this was the only traumatic life event that I was to endure, I believe that I would have survived it and got on and led a fairly normal life. But as is often the case, it was when I thought that I had turned a corner that life dealt me its foulest hand. As I grew into adulthood I put the abuse behind me (or so I thought) and got on with the business of living. It was while I was getting on with life that I met Annabelle. I met her one Saturday night in the pub after I had been playing rugby. When I saw her, I knew what love at first sight meant. Being psychotic has nothing on being in love. Love is without question the true psychotic experience. Annabelle was an artist; sculpture was her main medium, though she also painted and did sketching. In the short time that we were together, she taught me many things: she taught me what love was, how to make love, and most importantly how to love life. She also taught me to appreciate the arts, such as classical music, opera, and theatre. With her I began to discover a spiritual dimension to my life, though I hasten to add that this was not a religious thing.

Our relationship developed quickly from the torrid passion of new lovers to the passion that consumes those who are indeed soul mates. We spent as much time as we could in each other's company. Often we would sit up through the night talking and planning as couples do. We were planning our life together; this was normality at its best. But like all normality, madness was lurking underneath, waiting for its chance to pounce and consume us. And then one day it did.

Like the day I met Annabelle, the day our relationship ended was a Saturday. I had been playing rugby and went home with something for us both to eat. When I got in I called to Annabelle, asking her if she wanted tea or coffee. She didn't reply. I went into the living room and she was lying on the coach. I asked her again and still got no reply. I gave her a shake but she would not wake up. I rushed out of the house to a neighbour and asked them to phone an ambulance. They sped her to hospital and put her on a life support machine; she did not make it, and three days later she was pronounced dead. Annabelle had taken her own life. I never really found out why, but I know that I blamed myself. I don't know why I blamed myself, though it was to be many years before I stopped doing so.

When she died a large slice of me died also. I swore that never again would I get emotionally involved with anyone. Like many others, I suppressed all of my emotions about

Annabelle and her death. I continued with a semblance of existence that others called life. Like the abuse, I chose to pretend it never happened. And, as with the abuse, my feelings of grief and loss and hatred of the world festered inside, growing and growing, waiting for their chance to devour me.

The time for my emotions to overcome me finally arrived when I had an accident on the rugby pitch that put me out of the game forever. Barely weeks had passed since I was discharged from hospital (still on crutches) when I heard a voice for the first time. I was in my office waiting for the computer to deliver the results of some data I had inputted when a voice behind me said that I had done it wrong. I turned around but there was nobody there. I stopped what I was doing immediately, went to the pub and got drunk. I remember thinking that I was stressed and needed a break.

Within a short six-month period, the voice had been joined by other voices that spent most of the day screaming at me. I could not focus on my work and the only relief I got was drinking myself into oblivion. Eventually my boss told me I had four weeks to get my act together. Four weeks later I was out of work, losing my home and on my way (though I didn't know it then) to my first encounter with psychiatric services. In double-quick time I became a pitiful sight with an unkempt beard, dirty clothes, and more and more frequently drunk than sober.

Eventually I could not take any more and phoned the Samaritans, and after much talking went to see my GP. He ended the consultation with the words, 'I am going to arrange for you to see a specialist.' Fine, I thought; that would take a while. What a surprise I was in for. He took me out of his consulting room and asked me to wait in a small side room in the surgery. A few minutes later he returned with a nurse, who he told me would look after me while he arranged an appointment with the specialist. The only thing I remember about that wait with the nurse was how little she spoke. It was as if she was frightened to be in the same room as me.

My short wait ended some three hours later when the GP returned with another man; it turned out that he was the specialist that the GP had contacted. The specialist introduced himself, and told me that he was a doctor and had come to see me because my GP was concerned about me. It was here that I went through my very first one-hour Present State Examination. After the interview, the psychiatrist told me that I was ill and it would be better if I came into hospital for a short time. I told him where to shove his hospital and fled the surgery. Three days later I was dragged into the Royal Free Hospital, where I was once again subjected to a psychiatric interview, with the conclusion that I was suffering from schizophrenia.

The psychiatrist there told me that if I took medication then my voices and other symptoms would be eradicated and I would get better. He told me that the medication took about two weeks to work, and in no time at all I would be back to something like my old self. He was wrong. Two weeks went by and if anything I was worse, so I stopped taking the medication and decided to leave. This was when I discovered the real power of the system. I was put on a Section 2 of the Mental Health Act, which held me for up to twenty-eight days against my will. This was swiftly followed by a Section 3: a treatment order, which not only allowed them to detain me, but also to medicate me forcibly if necessary. This became my new way of life: a constant round of illness with short periods of respite (not wellness) in the community.

I was to spend six of the next ten years as an in-patient, almost all of them on a Section 3. In this time I had nearly forty sessions of electro-convulsive therapy (ECT), tried virtually every neuroleptic on the market, and was denied psychological interventions on numerous occasions. Despite the most vigorous of treatment regimes, the voices I heard remained as virulent as ever. Medication gave me no respite, and eventually the volume of medication I was taking was so high that I became little better than a zombie who viewed life through a legalised drug-induced smog.

The system did teach me things, the main one being how to be a good schizophrenic. I do believe that we learn much about how to be mentally ill in the system. Ten years were to pass before I found a way out the system, and by that time the system had created a perfect schizophrenic.

This learned behaviour is common. Even today, I meet people who have been taught that their lives are almost over. Graduates that are told they should give up any thought of a career; young people who are told they will achieve nothing in their lives. At the same time, society is trying to understand why so many young people kill themselves. This failure to relate the way we treat people to any type of negative outcome is perhaps the most damning indictment of our current system.

This hopelessness consumed me as I sat day after day achieving nothing, wanting nothing, expecting nothing, and getting nothing in return. Then, one day, it all changed.

Chapter Two

THE STEPPING STONES TO RECOVERY

In this chapter I intend to explore some of my personal stepping stones to recovery. These are my navigators (individuals who, through their support and encouragement, helped me steer my recovery journey); the mapmakers (those who charted the recovery course); the anchors who have kept me grounded and secure; and also the role of self, the role of people, and finally, the importance of ownership.

The reason I have chosen these particular elements (there are obviously many more) is that they played a clear part in my personal journey of recovery. This chapter is not intended to be a recovery model. Rather it is, if you like, a celebration of the diversity of the recovery process in that no two recoveries are the same. In effect I have written this chapter to highlight the idea of recovery as a journey.

Travelling the Recovery Road: Navigators

Any recovery journey has a beginning, and for me the beginning was meeting with my support worker Lindsay Cooke. It was her who encouraged me to go to the hearing voices self-help group in Manchester at the start of 1991. It was her, not me, who believed that a self-help group would benefit me. It was her who saw beneath my madness and into my potential. It was her faith in me that kick-started my recovery, and it is to her that I owe an enormous debt.

I remember meeting Lindsay: she was a bubbly, vivacious, all-moving sort of person who had dreadlocks in her hair and did not talk like a social worker (she had just qualified as one), but like an ordinary person (which she was). It was her ability to treat me as a normal person that fashioned the relationship that eventually created the pathway for me to leave the system. In essence, Lindsay was my holder of hope until I could hold that hope for myself.

There are other essentials required for a journey to be successful. One of these is the ability to navigate to your desired destination. In this I was fortunate to have not one navigator but many. In this section I will mention eight of them. The first is Anne Walton, a fellow voice hearer, who at my very first hearing voices group asked me if I heard voices, and when I replied that I did, told me that they were real. It does not sound like much, but that one sentence has been a compass for me, showing me the direction I needed to travel and underpinning my belief in the recovery process.

The second is Mike Grierson. Mike was the person who navigated me through my first contact both with my voices and with society. He encouraged me to go out and socialise with people who had nothing to do with the psychiatric system. He also took me to places like the cinema and classical concerts, which reawakened my love for the arts. Mike was not only my social navigator, he was one of the people who helped me to focus on my voices in a way that allowed me to explore the voice hearing experience more fully. As I reflect on the part Mike played in my life, I think that in many ways I have understated his role in past editions of this book. I must confess that it is much easier, with the benefit of over ten years of hindsight, to see the absolutely essential part that he played in reintroducing me to this strange place we call the world. I imagine that at times he must have been totally frustrated with my behaviour in the pub and other places, but he stuck with it. I now realise that Mike taught me what friendship can truly be like. I am sorry that it took me so long to get that message, but now that I have I will never forget it, and hopefully develop the same amount of patience in my relationships that Mike had in ours.

The third and fourth are Terry McLaughlin and Julie Downs. Terry and Julie were my navigators back to normality: they rekindled my interest in politics, and took me into their family without reservation. It was with Terry that I developed much of my early thinking around training and mental health. Later, alongside Julie as a co-worker, I continued to develop training packages that we used to explore the world of mental health. As I write these words, fourteen years after the first edition of this book, I think about the fact that Terry is no longer with us. His death came as a great shock, for to me he was the heart, as well as the conscience, of the hearing voices movement. At his funeral, which was indeed a celebration of his life, I watched the heart leave the movement. Julie was Terry's partner, and they were indeed soul-mates. When she was made redundant from the English Hearing Voices Network (HVN) because of a lack of funding, I felt that we had not only lost our heart, but we were now losing our soul. On reflection, that is what Terry and Julie gave back to me: my heart and my soul.

My fifth person is Paul Baker, another of my navigators on the road to recovery. Paul, who brought HVN to the United Kingdom, encouraged me to become involved in the Network, and then, when the time was right, handed over the development of voices self-help groups to me. To all of my navigators – Anne, Mike, Terry, Julie, and Paul – I owe my sanity.

I would like to explore the role that three other navigators have played in my life, and how my thinking, training, and practice have developed over the last twenty years. These three were not mentioned in this section of the first, or even second edition, as I had not yet developed the reflective skills that are required to see beyond what was right in front of me. Sometimes this is called the inability to see the woods for the trees.

The first of these was Dr Phil Thomas. I first met Phil in a café in Manchester. He was brought to meet me by Paul Baker, and others from Manchester HVN. The meeting was a strange one, as I was on the run from the psychiatric system and the police were looking for me. As I recall Phil never once mentioned the fact that he could get into serious trouble, first for not trying to get me to go back to hospital, and second for not reporting my whereabouts the minute he was free to do so. Phil played no small part in enabling me to remain working within the system, and stopped my drift towards an out-and-out anti-psychiatry position. Apart from Marius Romme, Phil was the first psychiatrist I had met that treated me as a person, and his humanity was the chief reason that I remain working to change mainstream psychiatry. The greatest thing he taught me was that I needed to be inside the system in order to change it. On a more personal note, Phil helped me gain access to my children, to whom I had been denied contact due to my mental health status. In a very real sense, Phil gave me back my identity as a father.

The second person in this trio is Ian Murray, sadly no longer with us. Ian died in 2009, and he was without doubt one of the best thinkers on self-harm in the UK. Ian and I spent many a day and evening (in the basement of his house as I recall) with small (well, not too small) glasses of whisky. He was able to articulate in a very clear way the interrelationship between self-harm and voice hearing as symbolic representations of intense emotional pain. He also helped me understand my own self-harm and supported me in investigating this: not as a professional, but as a friend. Without doubt my self-harm would still be a source of shame for me today if not for him. He did this by explaining self-injury as a form of communication (Sharon LeFevre [1996] later referred to this concept as intermediate language). This explanation made sense to me and allowed me to see my self-harm as a means of expression, not a reason for blame or shame. He also believed in the concept of safer self-harm (now called 'harm minimisation'). He was one of the people who helped me regain my pride.

The third person is Mike Smith, who I met in Birmingham one day at a meeting of the International Mental Health Network. He gave me a lift back to Manchester that evening, and as we drove we had a long argument about recovery and psychosis. As a result of our debate, Mike invited me to do training for his organisation. This resulted in me getting a job with him as part of the development team, which gave me the confidence to start thinking about becoming properly self-employed. It resulted in the formation of Action Consultancy and Training, and the publishing house Handsell. Mike was instrumental in the development of my future. Together we wrote *Working With Voices* (Coleman & Smith, 2006), which has now been translated into seventeen languages. Without doubt, Mike helped me regain my confidence in the world of work.

Travelling the Recovery Road: Mapmakers

Navigators require a map or plan from which to navigate. I have been fortunate, for the people who were my mapmakers were Patsy Hage, Marius Romme, and Sandra Escher. I do not believe that these three fully understand what they have done. Little did Patsy know when she read the book by Julian Jaynes (1976) that the questions this would make her ask were going to affect so many people. Indeed, it is because of her questions that HVN, Resonance, and other networks throughout the world exist today. Whether she wants it or not, she has a premier place in the history of the hearing voices movement.

Sandra Escher is without doubt the person who made sure that ordinary people could understand the maps that were being made. Her ability to communicate the message in language that was accessible to everyone has meant that the work has not remained in the world of academia, but has been used by voice hearers from the very beginning. Sandra and Patsy have played a very important part in my recovery.

The final mapmaker is Marius Romme. Marius, who in his own words is a traditional psychiatrist, is without doubt one of the greatest mapmakers who it has been my good fortune to know. When he listened to Patsy Hage and explored what she was saying, it was then in my opinion that he stopped being a traditional psychiatrist. When he asserted in public for the first time that hearing voices was a normal experience, and that voice hearing was not to be feared, he stopped being a traditional psychiatrist. And when he continued his work, despite being ridiculed and criticised by his peers, he stopped being a traditional psychiatrist and in my opinion became a truly great psychiatrist.

To Patsy, Sandra, and Marius I only owe one thing, and that is my life.

Travelling the Recovery Road: Anchors

So, these are some of the people who have helped shape who

I am today. There are of course many more characters that I could write about, but for most this would be an intrusion into their private lives. However, like most rules, there is an exception to it, and I will therefore intrude into one other person's life. Up to now you have been introduced to my turning points, my navigators, and my mapmakers. The final character has been all of these things and more to me: she has been the anchor in my journey over the last thirteen years.

I am of course talking about Karen, my wife. We both knew within a couple of hours of meeting each other that we had found the person we were destined to meet. We are a strange match at first glance. She is a psychiatric nurse, I was a psychiatric patient. She is beautiful, I am at best 'rugged'. She is an outdoor person who enjoys swimming in the sea and going for long walks, whilst I am an indoor person who enjoys watching sport on television and lounging around in the house. Nevertheless, in Karen I found not only love but also direction: she has encouraged me to develop myself not only in my work, but also in how I relate to people. With her I have learned that it is okay to argue and that it is not the end of a relationship. Through our children I have learned the joy of fatherhood, a thing I failed at miserably with my oldest children, though even they have now given me a second chance. With her I have started to explore my spiritual life. With her I am becoming me, Ron Coleman. What more can I ask for?

However, there is more. Karen has supported me through good times and bad; alongside her I have become a more rounded person, and we have become a real partnership in the work we do around mental health. Indeed I can honestly say that she is seeing me through my late-onset adolescence and my transition into the man I strive to be.

People

Up to this point I have mentioned twelve people who have been participants in one way or another in my recovery journey. And therein lies the first stepping stone to recovery: people. If I were to name all the people who have played a part in my recovery the list would be massive. The other thing about this list would be that the majority on it would not be professionals. One of my fundamental beliefs about recovery is that it cannot, and does not, happen in isolation. Nor can it happen if all our relationships are based on professional-and-client interactions. Recovery is, by definition, wholeness, and no one can be whole if they are isolated from the society in which they live and work. For many years I argued that there is no such thing as mental illness, and this led me into some interesting debates. One of these was with Marius Romme. During our exchange, it became clear that Marius was not arguing a case for biological illness; what he was saying is that illness could be expressed as a person's inability to function in society. This I can accept, as it means that recovery is no longer a gift from doctors, but the responsibility of us all.

This also raises the question of whether society is prepared to take any kind of responsibility for the recovery of people with mental health problems. I am of the opinion that they will not, for in our sophisticated culture we have bought into the notion of a biological explanation for mental health. I suppose that my expectations of society might appear to be too high, but that must be seen in the context of those societies that do accept responsibility for those amongst them who become mad. For example, in the Australian Aboriginal culture, when someone goes mad the whole tribe comes together to discuss what the tribe has done to cause the person to be mad. Can you imagine this happening in our society? I think not. When someone goes mad in our culture, it is off to the hospital with them. Local people do not gather together to decide what is wrong with the community; it is a ward round comprised of so-called experts who meet, often without the person concerned being present, who decide both what is wrong with the client and how this will be treated. This scenario, alas all too familiar, does not hold out much chance for recovery. It is an impersonal, rather than a person-centred way, of approaching the problem. Within this scenario recovery is objective, not subjective, and the person is no longer a real factor in the process.

The Self

I believe that much of what we call mental illness is based on a collapse of the self through the systematic destruction of relationships that validate the self. Such destruction often results in an individual becoming alienated from their society, in which relationships are formed. Within my own life, this can be seen in my relationship with spirituality (the abuse I received at the hands of a priest has clearly affected not only my view of priests, but also my view of all things spiritual). This has meant that I refused, at all levels of my life, to acknowledge the possible existence of my own self-spirituality. This is not a matter of whether I believe in a spiritual dimension or not, but a matter of protecting myself through refusing even to explore the possibility of the spiritual self. The need to protect myself is born out of my life experience at the hands of a spiritual leader, and at the point that the abuse started my relationship with spirituality was severed. If this were the fourteenth century my lack of spirituality would be deemed evil, a sign of possession or a perversity of the mind, and I might well end up incarcerated, or even executed. Without doubt my capacity to live and function during that period of history would be greatly affected by my inability to function at a spiritual level. Putting it another way, when I was young and wanted to become a priest, my self was validated through my relationship with God via the Catholic Church. When that relationship was destroyed, I did not suddenly stop believing in God. It was more that I felt alienated from God. My life at this point had lost its main validation, and as a consequence my life was in turmoil. My identity was being subjectively destroyed by my inability to hold onto self, and it seems clear that when working with those who are going through such experiences, we need to operate in a way that re-establishes the self.

The voices I experienced were external: that is, I heard them through my ears. I have already explored the voice of the priest; now I will explore the voice of my first partner, Annabelle. Annabelle was my first lover and the first woman I made any type of commitment to. When she died her death had a profound effect on me, and it determined much of my life from then on. I did not hear her voice until many years after the event, mostly due to the fact that I had suppressed both the loss of Annabelle and my abuse at the hands of the priest. This meant that I refused, on a conscious level, to have any internal dialogue with myself about these events. The result of this refusal was that I did everything I could to avoid these areas of my life, and consequently never dealt with any of the feelings that these traumas engendered.

As well as turning away from any spiritual dimension in my life, I also rejected any relationships that required a degree of commitment. Though I did these things unconsciously, it appears obvious to me now that the reason for doing so was to protect myself from further hurt. After all, my formative experience of relationships was that people either abused you or left you. In other words, I was struggling to protect my identity and to hold on to self. This means that denial (for that is what I was doing) had a primary protective function. Far from being a negative way of dealing with trauma, it can (in the short- to medium-term) be an adaptive way to shelter a fragile ego.

Suppressing one's feelings is a normal coping strategy that many people employ to protect themselves from adverse life events. I suppressed my feelings for many years before I was forced to face them, and I now believe that the reason I heard voices was my refusal to explore and deal with my own distress. Though I was not prepared to examine what had happened in my life on a conscious level, this did not mean that my unconscious mind was doing the same. Indeed, much of my thinking around my voices is based on my belief that they appeared in order to alert me to the fact that my life was not whole. What I mean by this is that when we endure a major trauma (and refuse to deal with it) we cannot successfully suppress our emotions forever: there comes a point when they must be dealt with. Continual refusal to acknowledge even the existence of a problem brings with it the need to adopt ever more extreme coping mechanisms (in my case, self-isolation and playing sport in a violent manner that went beyond the norm of the game). Indeed, the fact that my voices started after an injury that ended my rugby career is indicative of the short-term usefulness of distraction-type coping strategies. Stripped of my means for dealing with my past forced my inner self into the position of reliving my experiences. However, my continual refusal to acknowledge the past traumas left my inner self with no option but to externalise them through the introduction of voices. I believe that it was my refusal to use the opportunity presented to me to explore the voices when they first started that caused me to be hospitalised. This refusal (like that of many others) is partly based on the societal belief that voices equate with insanity. This was the belief that I held myself at the time, and the reality for me at that point was a simple one: I was mad. My secure self had vanished, to be replaced by a helpless and frightened self that felt controlled by the voices I heard.

Like many others it took me some time before I sought professional help and, like many others, the response of the professionals was typical: they saw my problem as a biological one and offered me medication. Like many others I rejected their formulation of my experience, and like many others I was forced into a conflict relationship instead of a recovery relationship with the psychiatric profession. Throughout this battle with psychiatry, a perverse emphasis was placed on the role of the self, in that my desire to be myself in the decision-making process about myself was assumed to reflect nothing more than a lack of insight on my part. The frightened self (which by this time had become very prominent) soon gave way to the angry-frightened self, which the professionals perceived as aggression, indicative of the deterioration of my illness. This in turn led to a continuation of the conflict, and a subsequent absence of recovery.

Thus, if people are the building bricks of recovery then the cornerstone must be self. I believe without reservation that one of the biggest hurdles we face on our journey to recovery is our relationship with self. Recovery requires self-confidence, self-esteem, self-awareness, and self-acceptance. Without this recovery is not only impossible, it is not worth it.

We must become confident in our own ability to change

our lives. We must give up being reliant on others doing everything for us; we need to start doing things for ourselves. We must have the confidence to give up being ill so that we can start being recovered. We must work at raising our self-esteem by becoming citizens within our own communities – despite our communities, if need be. We are valued members of our societies, and we must recognise our value. We need to recognise our own faults: the system may have created our diagnoses, but it is often ourselves who reinforce it. We need to change those behaviours that still trap us in our roles as patients. We need to accept and be proud of who and what we are. I can honestly say that my name is Ron Coleman and that I am psychotic and proud. This is not a flippant statement; this is a statement of fact.

I am convinced that when we grow confident about who and what we are, we can then be confident about who and what we might become. For me these four selves (self-confidence, self-esteem, self-awareness, and self-acceptance) represent the second stepping stone on the road to recovery.

The third step is closely related to the second, and it is rooted in our status. I believe that we ourselves have a great deal of say in our own status. We can choose to remain victims of the system: we can choose to continue to feel sorry for ourselves, we can choose to remain the poor little ill person who requires twenty-four-hour care from professionals. Or, on the other hand, we can choose a different direction. We can choose to stop being victims and become victors; we can choose to stop feeling sorry for ourselves and start living again; we can choose to stop being the poor little ill person and start the journey of recovery. This, for me, is the third stepping stone: choice. When we think of ourselves as ill, it is easy to let others make our choices. However, the recovery road demands that we not only make our own choices, but that we take responsibility for our choices, good and bad. As we make choices we will make mistakes, so we must learn to see the difference between making a mistake and having a relapse. It is the easy option to go running back to the psychiatric system when we make mistakes; rather than face our own weaknesses, we fall into the trap of blaming our biology rather than our humanity. If people are the building blocks of recovery, and self is the cornerstone, then choice is the mortar that holds the bricks together (see also Chapter Seven).

In concluding this analysis of selfhood, I must state that whilst I acknowledge that self must be rooted and understood in societal terms, it is equally the case that the notion of self becomes personal when the individual is alienated to such an extent that there is no collective with which they can engage. It is therefore evident that some form of collectivist approach is essential to any recovery process. Personally, I found this approach within a hearing voices self-help group. At the very first meeting I attended, a group member asked me the question, 'Do you hear voices?' and when I replied that I did, responded with, 'They are real, you know.' This validation of my experience, as well as the validation of my 'self', was a pivotal point in my recovery process. The self-help group became my community in a very real sense; it became the place where I could explore the meaning of self through talking with others. Indeed, in a strange way the group almost became The Self. I suppose the biggest change that occurred for me within it was that I stopped being Ron Coleman the schizophrenic and became Ron Coleman the voice hearer. Although this was only the beginning of the recovery process, it was a good beginning. I never cease to be amazed by the amount of people I meet that introduce themselves to me as their label: they say things like, 'Hello, my name is John, and I'm a schizophrenic.' I know there was a time when I did the same. However, I would never introduce myself with, 'Hello, I'm Ron Coleman and I'm a diabetic' (which I am) because being diabetic says nothing about my status in society (see also Chapter Four).

Ownership

There is one other stepping stone in the recovery process, and that is ownership. Ownership is the key to recovery. We must learn to own our experiences, whatever they are. Doctors cannot own our experiences; psychologists cannot own our experiences; nurses, social workers, support workers, occupational therapists, psychotherapists, carers and friends cannot own our experiences. Even our lovers cannot own our experiences. We must own our experiences. For it is only through owning the experience of madness that we can own the recovery from madness (see also Chapter Four).

Taking ownership was a major turning point in my journey as it meant that I had to take responsibility for my own life: I could no longer blame 'my illness' for everything that happened to me. It was not easy to do this, as like many I had accepted the victim role, handing power and autonomy over to the system. Reclaiming ownership is itself a process of reflection, recognition, planning, and action.

Reflection: It is often said that the beginning of anything is the hardest part, and this is true for the process of ownership. There is no doubt that taking time to reflect about yourself (and doing it in an honest and open way) is a frightening endeavour. I must confess looking at myself reflectively meant that I found parts of myself that I did not like – but it had to done.

Recognition: From my reflections I had to recognise and acknowledge those parts of my life and my personality that I could make changes in. I did this both by writing them down, and by discussing them with people I trusted.

Planning: Keeping a written record allowed me to then begin planning what I would do about the issues I had recognised in myself. I started by planning over a three-month period, as any longer time scale appeared unreal to me.

Action: The first three parts of the process are meaningless if there is no action. For me, it was important that I had within my plan something that could be done immediately, thereby kick-starting the reclamation of power and the ownership that comes with this.

The journey through madness is essentially an individual one. We can only share part of that journey with others; the greatest part of the journey is ours and ours alone. It is within ourselves that we will find the tools, strength, and skills that we require to complete this journey, for it is within ourselves that the journey takes place.

Recovery and Discovery

One question I am often asked is why I decided to make the transition from patient to trainer, speaker, and activist. To tell the truth, there is no single simple answer. As members of the hearing voices group in Manchester, we were encouraged to talk about – and own – our experiences within the group, and as the group developed we were often asked to talk to mental health teams, social workers, and others. The first time I spoke publicly was in Manchester at a small conference at which Marius Romme and Sandra Escher were the keynote speakers. I was very nervous, still taking a lot of medication, and when I stood up I read from notes. My presentation lasted about ten minutes and was delivered in a low stuttering voice, with shaking legs and no confidence. After the conference I went to the bar with Terry McLaughlin, Paul Baker and a few others. We sat with Marius and Sandra, and I said nothing but only listened as this pair talked with authority about the normality of the voice hearing experience.

With a lot of encouragement from Terry and Paul, I started speaking in public more often, ultimately becoming involved in developing hearing voices training alongside Terry. (This early work included the 'voice simulation exercise', which is now used in training and education sessions all over the world.) With this experience behind me, it was suggested that I speak at a conference in London. It was a very different me who turned up to this event: someone who stood up without notes, confident that I had a message to impart, that recovery was real, that it was here, and it was here to stay. Marius and Sandra were also present and after the conference we all went for a meal, during which Marius came up and asked me in a very Marius-type way (which to those that know Marius means that he told me) that I would be coming to Maastricht to speak at a conference.

This instruction from Marius was, if you like, the starting point of my current life. The conference was a great success and I have now spent the last seventeen years delivering and developing training and becoming involved in service development. This has been a journey of discovery as well as recovery: from my first fearful trip to America where I wore a kilt on the plane on the basis that if the plane crashed then they would know who I was because of my tartan (such was my fear of flying). Marius often talks about the suitcase I had at that time which was really old and held together by string. Nowadays I have no fear of flying, treating flights as I would a bus ride, and my luggage is in much better shape. If I had to describe this part of my journey in one word it would be growth.

Now as I reflect on the thirty years I have spent in the psychiatric system both as a service user and as a worker, I can truthfully say that I am proud of who I am. Another question I am often asked is whether I would change anything. And the answer to this is simply *no*. I now believe that everything I have gone through has had a purpose. I am by no means perfect, and I never will be. But most of the time now I am contented.

Recovery: An Alien Concept?

Recovery has become an alien concept, yet nothing I have talked about so far is based on rocket science. Rather it is based on common sense. It is not anything new, it is merely a reiteration of a holistic view of life. We need to realise that sometimes we make things much more difficult than they have to be. It is almost as if we need life to be a science that we never fully understand. We seem to spend much of our time making the complexities of living even more complex through our appliance of scientific objectivity, rather than exploring our lives through the simple mechanism of personal subjectivity. The time has come to have a close encounter with an alien concept. It is time for recovery.

Recovery is on the agenda – not clinical or social recovery, but personal recovery. The responsibility for recovery lies with us all: professionals, users, and carers. We can only achieve it by working together, and we can only achieve it by talking and listening to each other. We can only achieve it through shifting the paradigm from one of biological reductionism to one of societal and personal development. The work of Romme and Escher has started this paradigm shift, and it is up to all of us to continue this work until the shift has been made. Until we succeed, people will still be locked away from society because they hear voices, or see visions, or have different beliefs. Until we succeed, people will still be treated against their will, society will still fear madness, and civilisation will remain uncivilised. Recovery is our common goal. It is achievable now – let us not lose the moment; let us work together to make it happen. Let us put our past differences behind us and go forward into this new millennium with new confidence. Let us go forward in this new millennium with a new concept of wellness. Let us go forward in this new millennium under a united banner; let us go forward to recovery.

Chapter Three

Defining Recovery

The belief in recovery from serious mental illness is still almost nonexistent in Western psychiatry. In its place we have adopted the concept of maintenance and social control for those we deem to be mentally ill. This has been dressed up in the language of recovery, but the outcomes and treatment for those with mental health problems remains much the same. Does this mean that recovery is not possible for those classed as seriously mentally ill? Or is it merely that we would have to put too much effort into the present system in order to ensure a recovery process that would work for all? Or have we lost the knowledge and the skills that are required to work with people in a way that will enable recovery?

Mike Smith and I still hold the view that recovery is not only an alien concept for mental health professionals and carers, but for the users of mental health services themselves. Yet we fundamentally believe that recovery is not only the desired outcome for service users, but that it is possible for all service users to recover. Furthermore, we consider that one of the biggest hurdles facing a service user on their road to recovery is the psychiatric service that the user is in.

We have never doubted for a moment that the distress service users suffer is real; nor do we question the validity of their experience. We fully accept the fact that people hear voices that no one else can, or see things that others cannot see. Neither do we deny that some people have tactile or olfactory experiences that others cannot perceive, or have beliefs that are different and inconsistent from those of their peer groups. What we do not accept is the notion that people who continue to have these experiences are somehow biologically flawed and should hand their lives over to the psychiatric system.

Mental health services do little or nothing to dispel the myths that surround madness, and even when they do attempt to do something, it tends to be around educating people about a biological condition that they will at some point in the future find a way of curing. Psychiatrists have couched their profession in a scientific language that very few outside of the profession can understand. They have shrouded themselves within a discourse that alienates their clients and makes them sound as if they (the psychiatrists) understand the very secrets of the mind.

In the first edition of this book (Coleman, 1997) I wrote:

> As Mike [Smith] and I have developed our work, I have come to the sad conclusion that in most services recovery is not even on the agenda. This is not only true in the United Kingdom but throughout the Western world, and it is for this reason that I have decided to write this book. (p. 20)

Although the language of recovery is now everywhere, fourteen years on I still stand by the sentiments behind that statement.

I do not pretend to have all the answers. Indeed, I would claim to only have more questions. But a start must be made, and so let us begin our journey. Like any journey, we need to start at the beginning, and the beginning of this journey is in defining what we mean when we talk about recovery.

What do we Mean by Recovery?

When discussing recovery, we must first decide what we mean by the term. For example, we often hear of doctors saying things like: 'John is making a good recovery.' This sounds very positive, but actually it tells us nothing about John because we have no context in which to work. If John had just had both legs amputated, then the doctor's notion of recovery may well be that the operation has been a success and that the wounds are healing. John, on the other hand, may think that without his legs his life is over. If this is the case, can we really say that John is making a good recovery? Or is it the case that, like most things in life, recovery is a subjective rather than an objective concept?

The definition of recovery is one of the main differences that exists between me and many professionals involved in psychiatry. Too often, the professionals' view of recovery means little more than maintaining the patient in a 'stable condition', regardless of issues such as the adverse affects of medication, or even the expressed wishes of the client. For me, recovery is a much more personal construct. Indeed, it is a construct that in reality can only be defined by the person themselves. The notion of a good recovery implies the concept of the existence of a bad recovery, which should be a contradiction too far. Unfortunately, however, I do not believe that within the field of mental health it is a contradiction too far, but the reality of many service users.

Let us return to John for a moment. He has taken the view that his life is in effect finished, yet he will live. So what is he really saying? My opinion is that John is looking at the quality of his life rather than at the fact that his wounds are healing. For John, life without legs is not a viable proposition at this time. This may well change in the future as alternatives are pointed out to him, but at this stage in his journey there is no way that John would consider himself to have recovered. Indeed, he may never consider himself as recovered; but he will be discharged from hospital, and eventually from outpatients, and to all intents and purposes be recovered.

I would argue that the same is true in mental health, in that psychiatrists will assess recovery with measures that mean very little to the client. A good example of this is the continual use of symptom-rating scales as an outcome measure. These scales will tell us things like whether the person is still hearing voices, but will not tell us if they can now cope with them. Even the use of quality-of-life scales tells us very little about whether the person feels they have recovered or not.

Even at the beginning of our quest to understand the recovery process we face our first obstacle: that is, defining what it actually is. The two most common types of recovery talked about within the mental health system are clinical recovery and social recovery. The first question we must answer is what do these two models really tell us about our practice when they are applied to the recovery process?

Clinical Recovery

As the term implies, clinical recovery refers to the absence of symptoms, either as a result of them being eradicated by treatment, or because the treatment is suppressing or controlling them. It does not matter which of these definitions you use as much as the theory that underpins them. The essential concept of clinical recovery is that the recovery process occurs because of the effectiveness of the clinical treatment.

At first it surprised me that when I was reading *Essential Psychiatry* (Rose, 1994) as part of my research for this book, that the word 'recovery' could not be found within the index. I must confess, though, that when I had thought it through by looking at those I knew who were in the system, the sense of surprise faded and was replaced by that of foreboding. Undeterred, I searched other books – with the same results: no mention of recovery. So is there a relationship between clinical recovery and recovery? Or is clinical recovery only a form of language that psychiatrists have picked up from their medical colleagues in other disciplines?

Even when the word 'recovery' is discussed by psychiatrists, it tends to be viewed in a theoretical or historical setting rather than a practical one. Indeed, what is often considered when deciding pathways for a client is an abstract notion of recovery called *outcomes*. The psychiatric trade has in effect created a language that meets the needs of professionals, rather than those of the service user.

Spot the Difference

There are now two words that we have to define in order to explore what clinical recovery really means and, more importantly, what value clinical recovery has for service users. These are recovery and outcomes.

The *Oxford English Dictionary* offers us various definitions of 'recovery':

1. Regain possession or use or control of; acquire or find (out) again; reclaim.
2. Secure by legal process.
3. Retrieve; make up for; cease to feel effects of.
4. Hence ~ able.

5. Come or bring back to consciousness, health or Normal State, or position.

For our purposes, the definition that should be used is the one that takes health and normal state as its core statement. Is this the definition that is practiced within current psychiatric services?

When we look at the definition of 'outcome' in the dictionary, it offers only three words. These are: Result; visible effect. I would argue that psychiatry is based on an abstract notion of results and visible effects rather than on any meaningful definition of recovery. The use of a biased, outcome-focused approach to mental health carries with it the risk of alienating the client from the recovery process through the limited measures used to determine outcomes. This, in turn, limits the use of interventions to those that will achieve the predetermined outcomes desired by the professional. The preference for outcome rather than recovery measures has major benefits to professionals. One of these is that it allows practitioners and researchers within mental health to avoid the obvious contradiction that would have to be faced about clinical recovery. That is, if recovery is based on the clinical effectiveness of the treatment (and clinical recovery equates with wellness), it would also appear that the opposite is true – in that if someone did not clinically recover, then they would remain unwell. This surely also means that the treatment has been ineffective: in layman's terms, it has not worked.

Measuring the outcome rather than recovery makes sense for professionals, as the possibility for bad results or outcomes is as readily available as the possibility of good results or outcomes. If on the other hand we were to measure 'recovery', it would become distinctly uncomfortable for professionals, as we do not hear much said about bad recovery. Indeed, bad recovery does not exist: you either recover or you do not. Even the use of partial recovery is not something that lends itself to the debate. Or can a person be a bit of a schizophrenic?

One can therefore argue that outcomes are a way of sanitising the non-recovery process rather than measuring a recovery process in any meaningful way. This need to sanitise the non-recovery process is visibly rooted within the psychiatrist's need to use a medical frame of reference as a means to understand mental distress. It is clear that within the medical model there is little (or no) notion of recovery for those with conditions such as schizophrenia. Indeed, the emphasis when working with people described as having 'enduring mental illness' is always on maintenance (i.e. preventing relapse). This concept lies at the heart of clinical recovery: not the possibility of cure, but the probability of relapse. This probability model of care and treatment is the model most commonly applied with services. We may dress it up in fancy titles such as 'assertive outreach' or 'continuing needs services', but essentially it is a probability methodology. This by definition means that professionals must utilise a method of defensive practice, thereby rejecting even the possibility of recovery.

Defensive Practice

At the core of defensive practice (indeed, in the very notion of it) is neither beneficial practice for the client, nor any concept of clinical governance, but the almost paranoid fears of professionals that they might be held legally accountable if anything goes wrong. During a trip to the United States, I asked an American psychiatrist why he could speak and write so radically about the social and economic causes of schizophrenia, yet use so much medication on his clients. His reply was simple: he lived in constant fear of litigation from patients or their families if anything went wrong. He told me that in the event of a serious incident, his best defence would be to prove in court that he had been actively treating his client with drugs, as laid down by the American Psychiatric Association. This rationale also underpins many of the attitudes of the psychiatric profession in the United Kingdom. When a psychiatrist faces charges of negligence in the UK, his only defence is to cite members of his peer group to say that they that would have acted in the same way in the same circumstances. I am of the opinion that this means that the law is not interested in whether it was the right or wrong thing to do, but whether it is what other doctors would have done.

The consequence of this narrow view of right and wrong is that psychiatrists are safer when they continue to do only 'the done thing'. This in turn means that they will not take risks of any kind – not out of any fear for the client, but from fear of what might happen to them. This reduces the tool-kit at the doctor's disposal to the 'safe' options of medication, ECT, or radical surgery. This begs the question of how effective are the treatment tools available to doctors in terms of achieving recovery.

Medication

Most psychiatrists appear to be wedded to the idea that they must treat everyone with medication, and that it is only through the use of medication that people recover. The evidence for this view appears to be based on research funded with money supplied by the pharmaceutical industry (Mosher, Gosden, & Beder, 2005; Watkins, 2010). When attending conferences, I am constantly amazed by the number of research papers available from drug companies that prove how effective their products are in the treatment of conditions like schizophrenia. My amazement stems not only from the volume of papers, but from the fact that if the claims contained within these papers are true, then why are such a high number of people diagnosed as having schizophrenia still actively psychotic despite the medication?

I have never disputed the fact that for some people medication has produced life-changing and life-saving results, and that for these individuals the use of pharmaceuticals has had great benefits. Research has shown that fully 33% of people using neuroleptic medication recover to such an extent that they will no longer require psychiatric services (Watkins, 2006). However, this does not change the fact that for 66% of patients, medication regimes work in either a very limited way or not at all. In my opinion it is both dangerous and foolish to see medication as anything more than a short-term strategy when dealing with mental health problems. There are a number of reasons why I take this position, though I intend to explore only a few of these within this book.

The long-term effects of psychotropic medication are not fully known, especially those of the so-called atypical neuroleptics, or the new antidepressants such as Prozac. In my estimation, what we do know about the (so-called) side effects of medication should be enough to make psychiatrists rethink the long-term use of this type of treatment strategy. We know, for example, that at least one person a week dies as a direct result of neuroleptic medication, and that many clients perceive the side effects of medication as being worse than the symptoms that are being treated. Medics conveniently ignore this knowledge when they are talking to clients about the treatment they are receiving. Other factors, which have also been conveniently ignored, are issues such as personality changes that can occur as a direct result of medication. A good example of this is the number of people who have become aggressive and violent after starting to use Prozac. Add to this the incidence of people contracting neurological problems such as tardive dyskinesia after prolonged use of neuroleptics, and it is no wonder that many of us consider psychiatry to be in a constant state of crisis. Do not get me wrong: I for one would have liked nothing better than to have gone to hospital for a couple of weeks, taken my medication and been discharged, to all intents and purposes well. But this was not my experience and like many others, my condition did not improve in any meaningful way no matter what medication I was given. Despite this I have never had a problem with the use of medication as a treatment for those with mental health problems. What I do have a problem with is the misuse of medication, and its continuing usage even when there are no benefits to the client.

It is the constant misuse of medication that I particularly cannot understand. If medication does not help an individual in any way, how can its continued use be justified? The answer that many psychiatrists have to this question is to declare that it is not the medication that is failing the client, but that the client is failing the medication. It is common within psychiatry to describe someone who is not responding to medication as being 'drug-resistant' – even when they have an adverse response to the drug. Rather than say a drug is not working, they find it easier to blame the person's own biology or physiology for the treatment's ineffectiveness. The professional response to this type of client beggars belief. Many of these individuals are subjected to ever-increasing dosages of medication, and the practice of polypharmacy amongst this group is staggering.

The more I have read about medication and how it works, the more I have become convinced that a client does not need to be tried on every drug within a grouping that is available. I would argue that, in the case of neuroleptics, there are only two types available (typical and atypical) and that if a person is tried on one of each and they fail, then surely there is no point in continuing to try other drugs within the same group. The only argument that can be even remotely valid is the need to change medication that is working in order to decrease the adverse side effects a person may be getting.

There is very little in common between these types of medication regimes and a truly person-centred approach to recovery. It is this absence of a person-centred approach that most condemns pharmacological treatments. Frequently medication is not worked out on an individual basis for the client, but rather on macro factors worked out by the pharmaceutical industry based on clinical trials using poor methodology (Breggin 1994; Mosher et al., 2005; Watkins 2010).

One of my friends, the consultant psychiatrist Phil Thomas, often talks about two levels of drug intervention. The first level, especially when prescribing anti-psychotics, is based on the usage of small doses of drugs (he calls this the therapeutic dosage). The second level of intervention is when a high dosage of drugs is used: he calls this social control. In his book *The Dialectics Of Schizophrenia* (Thomas, 1997), he writes:

Concern about the use of high doses of neuroleptic medication has focused on two areas in particular. Many psychiatrists and psychiatric nurses working in in-patient units feel that the conditions found in these units contribute to the need to use high doses of medication. (p. 122)

He then points out that in his experience, junior doctors were called out more frequently to write up prescriptions when there where fewer staff on duty. What this indicates is the relationship between environment and how clients respond or feel. This should not come as any surprise, but it appears that for many professionals the correlation between environment and symptoms somehow eludes them.

The next area of concern that Thomas writes about is the treatment of young black men. He writes:

The second worry concerns the use of high doses of medication in particular groups, particularly young Afro-Caribbean men. This has almost certainly contributed to the sudden death of a number of young black men over the last ten years. (Ibid, p. 122)

Thomas then concludes that an enquiry (Special Hospital Service Authority, 1993) suggests that the reason for the high dosage of drugs in this group was a reflection of:

… crude stereotypes that black men were potentially dangerous. White health professionals often find it difficult to conceal the fact that they perceive young black men as 'dangerous' or 'violent' and it is for this reason that this group is liable to receive higher doses of neuroleptic medication. (Ibid, p. 123)

It is not surprising that many Afro-Caribbean people I know who have used our services describe the white professionals who are treating them as 'dangerous' or 'violent'. In any other area of our lives, such as in employment or education, treating black people in this way would be seen as racial discrimination. Probably the only other institution acting in the same way with the same impunity is the police force. Perhaps this is one more piece of evidence that psychiatry is often used within society as an agency of the state: enforcers of social control.

The use of medication in this way is nothing new, and historically we have often attempted to deal with social problems using chemical solutions. One of the most infamous examples involved the use of Valium, which was prescribed to tens of thousands of people from the 1950s through the 1970s (mainly women) who were finding it difficult to cope with their domestic environment. The drug never dealt with the problems of their home lives. What it did do, however, was to create tens of thousands of drug addicts (Lexchin, 1998; Metzl, 2003; Tone, 2008). These women were not turned into addicts through choice, but through the short-sightedness of the medical establishment and the greed of the drug companies. This disaster is in the process of repeating itself, as we now find the newer drug Prozac being prescribed for many of the same reasons that Valium originally was. Despite assurances from drug manufacturers that it is not addictive, there have already been cases of addiction reported (Peele, 2005) and no doubt in time we will pay the same high price for our failure to learn the lessons of history.

Another common belief about medication is that people who stop taking it will always relapse. This view appears to be supported by research such as that carried out by Dencker,

Lepp, and Malm (1980), which reported on the withdrawal experiences of 32 patients from depot neuroleptics. After six months, 50% of the sample had experienced symptom relapse, and after twelve months this rate had risen to 81%. Though this is a very high relapse rate, the study does not tell us anything about the quality of life for the client group after their symptoms reappeared. There is also the fact that 19% had no reoccurrence of symptoms, yet our system would still insist that they remain on their medication over a long period. For this 19%, the evidence suggests that medication is not needed, though in many countries individuals may well be forced to take medication in the community through the system's use of Mental Health Law. If 19% of people in our prison system were being held for crimes they did not commit, there would be an international outcry about the miscarriages of justice being perpetrated by the state.

The reason I have used this study is that it reports one of the highest relapse rates. Other studies have described much lower levels. For instance, Gitlin et al. (2001) found that while 78% of 53 patients experienced 'symptom exacerbation' within one year of discontinuing neuroleptics, only six individuals (11%) experienced clinically significant relapse requiring hospitalisation. In trials where placebos were used, Pasamanick et al. (1964) found that 45% of the group on placebos relapsed over an 18-month period, whilst Hirsch et al. (1973) found that 50% of the group on placebos relapsed over a nine-month period. Weiden and Oltson (1995) examined national relapse rates in the US for patients diagnosed with schizophrenia, and found that the monthly average for those on maintenance neuroleptics was 3.5%, and only 11% for those who discontinued medication. More recent research by Harrow and Jobe (2007) compared the outcomes of 145 patients over fifteen years to determine whether unmedicated individuals could function as well as patients taking antipsychotic medications. The data suggested that the patients not taking medication showed significantly better global functioning and longer periods of recovery.

I believe these results to be a damning indictment of the psychiatric system, as they challenge the value of concentrating on medication strategies in the treatment of those labelled as seriously mentally ill. The fact that in one of the studies (Pasamanick et al., 1964) 65% of patients taking placebos (that is, not on medication) did not relapse must at the very least generate doubt in the present understanding of the causes of the mental distress: in this case, the dopamine theory (Hutton, 2010). If we extrapolated this to figures rather than percentages, it would mean that out of 1,000 people on neuroleptic medication, 650 would find the same benefits from taking a placebo as they would from taking the real thing. They would also be without any of the adverse effects caused by the use of neuroleptics. Such figures also point to the inherent dangers in basing practice on a theory that has not been proven.

Stopping Medication: a Dangerous Dilemma

For many, the predicament they face when stopping medication has less to do with relapse, and more to do with the consequences of withdrawal. Breggin, in his classic book *Toxic Psychiatry* (1994), writes:

> Because of the withdrawal problems, patients should try to come off the medications while receiving emotional and social support from others and with supervision by someone familiar with the

process. It should be understood that withdrawal symptoms may encourage the doctor and the patient alike to resume the drug prematurely, when what the patient really needs is time to recover from the drug. (p. 108-109)

What Breggin is clearly spelling out in this extract is something that many of us have speculated about for a long time: the addictive qualities of psychotropic medication in general, and neuroleptic medication in particular. How often do doctors tell their clients that the effects they feel when they stop their medication are due to relapse, rather than anything to do with the withdrawal from the drug(s)? At worst, this is another example of the misinformation that professionals give users and carers, and at best it shows how badly informed professionals are themselves. Either way it is a sad reflection on the ability of the psychiatric system to face up to its responsibilities to those who are subjected to its ministrations. For myself, coming off neuroleptic medication was one of the most difficult things I have ever done. Even though I thought I understood what was going to happen to me when I stopped the medication (I was forced to go cold turkey, because my psychiatrist would not support a reduction regime) nothing could prepare me for the reality of withdrawal. Apart from sweating and shivering, being sick, and unable to sleep, I heard even more voices than normal. I had visions (something I had never experienced before), out-of-body experiences (again new), and my thinking became chaotic and confused. Add to this a developing paranoia, and you can see that throughout the withdrawal process I was a prime candidate for hospital admission on the basis of relapse due to noncompliance. After four weeks of this my condition improved quickly, and within another three weeks I was as near to being myself again as I ever had during the ten years I spent in the system. Reflecting back on this experience, it is not something I would recommend. It would be better by far if those suffering from mental distress were given the right to opt for drug-free alternatives and given the support they require to withdraw from their medication in a safe and structured way (Hall, 2007). The British government, however, seems to think it knows what is best for those with mental health problems. In 1998, they began a review of psychiatric services on the grounds of collecting evidence-based practice to ensure good clinical governance. In almost the same breath, the Minister of State also claimed that for those deemed to be mentally ill, noncompliance was not an option. In one sentence, the government had declared the answer to something that has been the subject of heated debate for the last century, by effectively stating that mental illness is a biological condition and that the way to treat it is to ensure compliance with medication. In the House of Commons in December 1998, the then-Minister of Health, Frank Dobson, declared he did not care what the experts thought: what mattered is what he thought, as he was the minister responsible.

In the UK, this unholy trilogy of the government, the Royal College of Psychiatry and the pharmaceutical industry, are relying on organisations such as SANE (Schizophrenia: A National Emergency) to spread its gospel of enforced compliance. This unholy alliance is without doubt using all the resources at its disposal to undermine any alternative views on the way forward in treating those experiencing mental distress. Medication is not, and never will be, the solution that will cure all those suffering from mental health

problems. Rather, it will (at best) provide some relief for some people. To rely on medication is, in my opinion, folly that verges on negligence. If compliance is ever to become a reality, then service providers must supply treatments that are based on client choice. If we make the choice to partake in a treatment regime, then surely it follows that we will comply with that regime?

Electroconvulsive Therapy (ECT)

ECT is the second treatment within the psychiatrist's tool-kit and, as the doctor sees it, is a tool with which she hopes to repair the damage that mental illness has inflicted on the patient. Of all the treatment options available to psychiatry, ECT is probably the most controversial, in that it is at the centre of an ongoing acrimonious debate between users and psychiatrists. In the UK, organisations such as ECT Anonymous and the All Wales User and Survivor Network are calling for either the suspension of compulsory ECT, or the banning of the treatment altogether.

One question I seek to answer in this book is: does ECT have a place within the recovery process of people defined as having mental health problems? The starting point in answering this question is to understand what ECT is, and what it does to people who receive it.

ECT is the passage of an electrical current through the brain in order to produce what are known as grand mal convulsions (epileptic fits). The theory is that the passage of electricity and the accompanying fit will stimulate brain activity in such a way that the person receiving the treatment will recover. Although it is primarily a treatment for depression, it is used for clients with various diagnoses (including obsessive-compulsive disorder ([OCD], hypermania, and schizophrenia to name but a few).

The most common response to the question, 'How does ECT work in terms of the recovery process?' is that no one really knows (Giles, 2002), but that for some people it does work, and in cases of severe depression it can work very quickly (Reisner, 2003). Indeed, many professionals have told me that without ECT some of their patients would die through self-neglect or suicide. It should also be pointed out that the same claim has been made by a number of people who have received ECT (e.g., Hartmann, 2002; Koopowitz, Chur-Hansen, Reid, & Blashki, 2003). Nevertheless, despite the assertions made by those who are pro-ECT, I am now convinced that it should be banned on the grounds that there is no place for it within psychiatric practice. The reason I have taken this position on ECT is simple: I have explored the facts surrounding ECT and have reached the conclusion that the establishment has been less than honest about what it does to the recipient. I will now lay out the facts I considered in coming to this conclusion.

There are seventy-six NHS Trusts currently providing ECT in England, and in the last twenty years the number of people receiving ECT whilst detained under the Mental Health Act has increased (Bickerton, Worrall, & Chaplin, 2009). According to the most recent figures from the Department of Health (DoH, 2003), there were 12,800 administrations of ECT in the UK during 2002. Of the 2,300 patients receiving the treatment, only 40% gave their consent. In fact, I would argue that the notion of informed consent in the UK is a farce, and indeed that informed consent is rarely given, as the client is not provided with the necessary information to ensure that consent is genuinely informed. Many of us now talk about the need for *real* consent, based on a full disclosure of information pertaining to the treatment.

For years now, psychiatrists have told patients that they did not know how ECT worked (Johnstone, 2000). This has not been the complete truth. Since the very early days of ECT, supporters of the treatment have been clear that the main reason it works is because of the damage it does to the brain.

The evidence that ECT damages the brain is well documented. Animal research conducted in the 1940s and 1950s clearly demonstrated that even small doses of ECT induced cell death and small brain haemorrhages. Hans Hartelius (1952) was able to tell which cats had received ECT by microscopic examination of their brains. There is evidence from post-mortem examinations of similar cell death and brain haemorrhaging in humans who have had ECT (Breggin, 1979, 1997; Read, 2005; Sterling, 2000; Templer & Veleber, 1982).

In *Electroshock: Its Brain-Disabling Effects*, Peter Breggin (1979) points to other evidence that indicates ECT's damaging impact, including neuropsychological testing, brain scan and brain imaging research, and other clinical reports. These studies all show damage to the brain and/or psychological functioning that can only have been caused by ECT. Furthermore Breggin, who deems ECT an 'electrically-induced closed-head injury' (1994, p. 232) notes the similarities between those who have had ECT and those suffering from brain trauma, stating that:

> I evaluated [the patient] and my clinical impression was generalized brain dysfunction with memory impairment, relatively shallow emotional responses, poor judgement, difficulty with intellectual functions, and problems focusing

attention. He had ... global mental deterioration –
caused by shock treatment. (Ibid, p. 230)

Surely this in itself is sufficient to show that brain
dysfunction is caused as a direct result of ECT? Max
Fink, one of the leading advocates of ECT administration,
accepts as much. Fink concedes that both the denial and
euphoria experienced by those who have received ECT are
directly linked to the amount of brain damage done by the
treatment. Indeed, Fink goes further when he claims that
brain dysfunction is neither a complication nor a side effect,
but the 'Sine qua non of the mode of action' (quoted in
Breggin, 1994, p. 244). In other words, Fink is relating the
effectiveness of the recovery process to the propensity of
ECT to cause brain damage. Fink is no radical campaigner
trying to stop ECT. Indeed, he is the opposite. The reality of
what he is advocating for those who have a mental health
problem is simple: brain damage is good for you.

The known adverse effects of ECT include death, brain
damage, memory loss, seizures, suicide, and personality
changes (Breggin, 1998; Giles, 2002, Read, 2005; UK ECT
Review Group, 2003), all of which can also be detected in
head injury patients. The decision our society must make
seems clear: is it justifiable to cause deliberate brain damage
and call it making people better?

Psychosurgery

The third tool available to the biological psychiatrist is
psychosurgery. Though not often talked about, it is still
an available option as a form of treatment. The practice
of operating on people's brains is not something new.
Historically, we can trace the practice back to the ancient

Egyptians, and throughout history, especially during times of war, surgeons related physical injury to the brain to altered emotional states.

Doctors came to the inevitable conclusion that if head injury could cause psychological changes, then deliberately mutilating portions of the brain would induce similar effects. Over sixty years ago, researchers showed that certain nerve pathways between the limbic lobe and the frontal cortex were central to the control of mood. By dividing these nerve pathways they discovered that they could relieve high-anxiety states and replace them with euphoric states. According to Walter Freeman, an early enthusiast for the technique, the procedure obtained its best results when conducted on women, Jews, black people, and those with manual jobs (Johnstone, 2000).

Egas Moniz developed the operation that we now call a leucotomy in the early 1900s (Moniz, 1937/1994). The procedure was claimed to be an effective treatment for schizophrenia, OCD, and depression. This effectiveness is brought into question by the fact that, according to the *Psychiatric Dictionary* (Hinsie & Campbell, 1970), disturbances caused by the operation included:

> Convulsive seizures... Post-operative blunting of
> the personality, apathy, and irresponsibility ...
> distractibility, childishness, facetiousness, lack of
> tact or discipline, and post-operative incontinence.
> (p. 438)

Michael Haslam, a supporter of psychosurgery, explains that the surgical methods used have advanced so far that the dangers of adverse physical effects are rendered minimal (though the psychological and emotional changes remain the

49

same). He does, however, acknowledge the real possibility of damage, although justifies the procedure as a legitimate last resort for patients who cannot be assisted in any other way. This 'ends justifying the means' approach is a common rationalisation within psychiatry. It also emphasises one of the major bones of contention between the psychiatrised and the psychiatrist: that is, the issue of who is in control of what happens.

Many people are surprised to learn that psychosurgery is still used, and some express disbelief and anger that it happens at all. Like many others I assumed that surgery was an extreme, last-resort treatment for violent schizophrenics. It was only when I started researching this form of surgery that I discovered how wrong I was. A review of recent literature indicates that psychosurgery is still being performed for patients with depression (e.g. Kim & Lee, 2008), OCD (e.g. Christmas et al., 2009), and paraphilias (e.g. Greenfield, 2006). In one survey of 85 patients who had been operated on, diagnoses were: depression (n=24); anxiety (n=20); obsessional compulsive states (n=19); violent behaviour (n=6); anorexia nervosa (n=5); intractable pain (n=4); schizophrenia (n=4), and self-destructive behaviour (n=3). In fact, only 15% of the sample fitted in any way, shape, or form with my preconception of the type of patient who would be referred for psychosurgery.

Essential Psychiatry (Rose, 1994), which actually has little to say on the subject, points out that psychosurgery is effective as a treatment for intractable obsessional and depressive disorders, and is only indicated after prolonged use of conventional treatments has failed. On the effectiveness of such surgery it is stated that:

The usual result of the operation is a reduction in

anxiety and tension. As a result treatments such as behaviour therapy that have previously been unsuccessful may now produce a remission in symptoms. (p. 191)

Despite early claims of its success as a treatment for those who might otherwise never have left hospital (especially those prone to violent mood changes), the role of psychosurgery as a tool for recovery is obscure to say the least, if not entirely unfounded. At the present time there is an almost unanimous belief amongst professionals that not only should it be the treatment of last resort, but that it should be carried out only on selected patients after long deliberation. These are not surprising beliefs, given that there have been no controlled evaluations of psychosurgery, mainly because the nature of treatment renders such an investigation problematic.

In light of this, and of the emphasis being placed on evidence-based practice founded on quality research, I find it hard to understand why such a procedure is still allowed to continue.

Damage Limitation

Clinical treatments for people with mental health problems seem to have the concept of damage limitation at their centre, rather than real recovery. This medical approach to mental health is without doubt based on treating symptoms and behaviour as opposed to treating causes, and such attitudes are dehumanising in that they reduce the mind to the role of a by-product of the brain. The position of the patient is also clearly defined within this framework as that of a passive recipient, whose only part in the process is to be compliant and not to complain about their treatment. This compliance is expected, despite the fact that the adverse effects of all the treatments on offer may be worse for many patients than the 'illness' that is being treated. Within mental health, the emphasis on compliance is now so great that we have created specialist mental health teams whose role is to ensure conformity to treatment regimens. In the UK, the Minister of State responsible for mental health repeatedly claimed in 1998 that noncompliance was not an option for those deemed to have enduring mental health problems. But compliance does not increase the number of people who recover from mental health problems, and neither does coercion. If we are to succeed as a society in enabling people to find a route to recovery, then we must stop reducing everything to biology.

There is a real need to exceed the limited tool-kit that is available to the biological psychiatrist in their quest to enable recovery. For the patient, the psychiatrist's tool-kit is a double-edged sword. Although biological and physical interventions appear to have benefits for some, we must ask ourselves the following question: is the damage these treatments can cause too high a price to pay for so-called clinical recovery?

Social Recovery

As with the concept of clinical recovery, our starting point must be a working definition of what social recovery is. Unlike clinical recovery, such a definition is complicated due to the differing contexts in which the word 'social' is used within the field of mental health. For the purposes of this section, emphasis will be placed upon the behavioural construct of social recovery, which views the recovery process as the person's ability (or lack of) to interact in a particular way within society. The reason for using this type of definition is that it is the one that most professionals seem to endorse when talking about social recovery. Warner, in *Recovery from Schizophrenia: Psychiatry and Political Economy* (2004) attempts to define social recovery as an outcome measure stating:

> If outcome is measured in terms of social functioning, the investigator may look at any combination of a range of features including the following: working ability, capacity to care for basic needs, abnormal behaviour causing distress to others, criminal activity, number of friends, or sexual functioning. (p. 61)

This definition warrants close scrutiny so that we can test whether it is valid to define social recovery under these terms (in effect: economic and residential independence, and low social disruption). However, I believe that throughout his definition of social recovery, Warner (partly by the demands of the research methodology) is forced to use measures that are judgmental, value-laden, and smack of high morals. In fact, in order to be socially recovered within this definition, a service user would have to be more normal than normal.

Economic and Residential Independence

For myself, the obvious flaw in the criteria that Warner employs to define social recovery is that many of the elements he uses to measure it are areas of our lives over which we have little or no control. Indeed, Warner himself concedes that in a climate of constant economic flux, individuals have only limited control over their employment opportunities. The economic cycle of boom and bust lends itself to periods of high joblessness, and it is evident that during times of low economic activity and spiralling unemployment, individuals with mental health problems are high in the priorities of employers who are looking to shed workers. It is equally evident that they are low in the priorities of those employers who are looking to recruit staff.

Even in times of boom when the economy is vibrant, the outlook for those seeking employment who are, or have been, in the psychiatric system is bleak. This is often due to the stigma that is prevalent in society. Economic independence via sustained employment is nothing more than a pipe dream for many service users. In fact the reality facing most people termed as having enduring mental health problems is one of long-term economic dependence.

If those with long-term problems spend most of their adult lives economically dependent on the state, then we must (using the above definition of social recovery) conclude that for this group social recovery is not a possibility. One way in which professionals who believe in this model of social recovery have squared this circle is to replace the emphasis on economic independence through real employment with a variety of alternatives based on the concept of 'meaningful activity'. These alternatives normally include sheltered employment and supported employment, although such options do not create economic independence for service users, but rather for the professionals who are paid to operate such schemes. In his definition, Warner talks about working ability, yet there can be little doubt that many service users who want to work, and have the ability to work, are stymied by the inability of society to accept their contribution as valid.

For many clients, economic independence is a myth (as

is, through extension, residential independence). Yet if these two fundamental factors are not in place, then our ability to care for our basic needs must surely be disrupted. The reality is simple: the process of institutionalisation and stigmatisation for people who are, or have been, in the psychiatric system engenders a process that robs them of economic and residential autonomy. In turn, this creation of dependency leads to the loss of a client's ability to care for her basic needs. It is somewhat ironic that one of the measures used to determine the level of a person's inability to function socially is only there because of the system's ability to create dysfunctional people.

Abnormal Behaviour

The next part of the definition, abnormal behaviour causing distress to others, is a similarly problematic construct that is open to considerable abuse through the interpretation of what constitutes 'abnormal'. Using subjective criteria, professionals cannot help but make judgements and reach conclusions based on their own values, prejudices, and expectations. Without doubt, these values (especially in the case of the medical profession) do not necessarily reflect the values of society as a whole. Rather they reflect the values of a privileged grouping within society.

If we were to apply this criteria to professionals how would they fare? In 1999, one of my friends was detained against her will in an English psychiatric hospital. The team who were looking after her decided during a review of her care that she should be denied any contact with family or friends. This was to include no visitors at all, no telephone calls, and no writing or receiving of mail. The decision was taken without consultation with my friend, and her advocate was not allowed to be present at the meeting (indeed, during this enforced isolation he was not permitted to visit her). The family and friends of this woman were deeply distressed by the attitude and behaviour of the staff, both towards themselves and towards her. I for one would argue that apart from a complete disregarding of human rights the team, through their abnormal behaviour, caused distress to others. This is not an isolated case that I had to rack my brains for hours to find, and it would be all too easy to cite many others that confirm this view. Perhaps the most interesting thing to note is that following the logic of the definition of social recovery that we are exploring, in this area at least we can conclude that professionals have a long way to go to achieve their own recovery.

Criminality

The remainder of the measures used by Warner, far from adding clarity to the concept of social recovery, actually confuse the issue further. The emphasis that is placed on criminal activity creates the impression that one of the symptoms of mental illness is the quality or state of being a criminal. I find this idea abhorrent in the extreme, in that it creates an unjustifiable stereotype of the behaviour patterns of those diagnosed as mentally ill. Organisations such as SANE have jumped on this imagined relationship between criminality and mental health by frequently issuing dramatic, unsubstantiated claims about the relationship between violence (especially homicide), mental illness, and failures of care in the community schemes to the mainstream British media.

The reality, typically, appears to be somewhat different. Research carried out by Taylor and Gunn (1999) on behalf of the Institute of Psychiatry discovered the following: in 1972, 356 people were convicted of homicide, 36.5% of which had a mental health problem. In 1979, 25% of the 480 homicides were perpetrated by individuals designated mentally ill, and in 1995 this level fell even further (11.5% of 522 convictions). Since 2000, the rate of homicide due to a psychiatric disorder in England and Wales has been 0.07 per 100,000 cases (Large et al., 2009). Further research in the UK by the Institute of Psychiatry (2006) suggests that 95% of homicide convictions are for people with no history of mental health problems. Indeed, service users are far more likely to be the victims of violence, intimidation, and exploitation than the perpetrators.

These figures fly in the face of claims made by the media and organisations such as SANE. The massive reduction in homicides committed by people with a mental health problem does not change the fact that every time a homicide does occur it is a tragedy for all those involved. What it does do, however, is to put into perspective the scale of the problem.

There is no doubt that people with mental health difficulties do get involved in criminal activity, but given that at least 25% of the population experience a mental health problem at some point in their lives, this should come as no great surprise. Once again, the main problem in this area is one of perception. The actions of the media have done much in conditioning the general public in relating 'mental illness' to criminality, risk, and dangerousness.

The real crime is the fact that most clinicians are using criminal activity as a measure of social recovery. This cannot but reinforce the belief that there is a definitive relationship between 'mental illness' and crime. Using criminality as an indicator of social recovery is unjustifiable and should have no place in any modern mental health system.

Social Relationships

Using the number of friends one has as a measure of social recovery is also deeply misleading, not least because it is often based on a subjective notion of the number of friends a person ought to have. This figure will frequently be derived (or at least influenced) by the individual professional's view of the number that is appropriate. In other words, it is often based on the number of friends that the professional has. This could be a major problem for users if the professional working with them is a sociable person. The number of friends we have is influenced by factors other than our personality: these factors are varied and many, and for the purposes of this book I will refer to them as opportunity factors. Opportunity factors include such things as having sufficient income to go out and meet people, having links in the local area with people who share common interests, and the level of medication you are taking. I imagine that the first question people might ask is, 'How can levels of medication affect the number of friends a person has?' For some, the answer to this question is obvious. For many, however, the relationship between social functioning and medication has not been established and therefore there is a lack of clarity around the issue. From my perspective, there is no doubt that the amount and types of medication a person is on will affect their ability to function at a social level. Using high levels of chemicals to control symptoms means that many clients spend much of their time in a drug-induced stupor, with some spending up to twenty hours every day in bed. The effects of medication in itself causes much of the social dysfunction, and most certainly disables many clients to the extent that they will find it nearly impossible to start and maintain the social contacts that will lead to friendships forming.

The over-prescription of medication denies people opportunities to do many things that most members of society take for granted. The last measure of social recovery, sexual functioning, is a classical example of the poor understanding of cause and effect relationships that exists within the psychiatric system. If a client is spending twenty hours a day in bed and experiencing extreme sedation, blunted emotion, tremors, nausea, diarrhoea, and weight gain (all common side effects of most neuroleptics) then it is very likely that his or her sex life will be limited. Even on small doses of medication, there is no doubt that many clients' sexual functioning is affected in a detrimental way (for example, male impotence, and inability to reach orgasm in both genders). Once again, the measure is flawed in that it does not take into account the effect that (possibly enforced) treatment is having on the person.

Methodology

Given that medication can confound client outcomes in every one of the measures employed by Warner, I would argue that the methodology he adopts to assess social recovery is fundamentally flawed. Furthermore, I would argue that much of the work done around social recovery is not about recovery at all. Rather,   it is about coping, making the best of things, and accepting responsibility. This process may make life easier for all concerned when it is successful, but it is not a process of recovery. Rather, it is what I would call a process of non-recovery that perpetuates the client's dependence on the system.

Others use a similar methodology. Paul Carling (1995), in a position paper on recovery, lays out the 'Basic Tasks of Recovery', as adapted from work by Curtis (1997) and Copeland (1997).

These tasks are listed as follows:

1. Increasing self-understanding about one's identity; patterns of behaviour; environmental, attitudinal, behavioural, interpersonal, or spiritual 'triggers'; and successful coping strategies, as well as preferred professional interventions and supports.

2. Identifying the need for, and arranging medical care and medications when necessary.

3. Crisis planning, including a list of symptoms that indicate assistance needed in making decisions, and a list of family members, supporters, and professionals who are authorised to make decisions in a crisis. A list of preferred, acceptable, and unacceptable medications, treatment facilities and information about care of children, pets or other tasks that need to be taken care of during the crisis.

4. Building a support system, including friends, family, peers and others.

5. Developing ongoing coping, monitoring and responding strategies, such as distraction, 'fighting back', seeking help, improving one's situation, self-soothing or escaping.

6. Developing advocacy skills and strategies to assure that one gets what one needs in the mental health system.

7. Developing a lifestyle that supports wellness, including valued roles, nutrition and exercise, sleep, light relaxation and private time, companionship and intimacy, pleasurable activities, pets, positive living space, meaningful activities and opportunities to contribute, and spiritual practice.

8. Incorporating these knowledge and skills into a personal Wellness Recovery Action Plan.

9. Addressing any specific issues that are relevant to one's recovery.

The use of this type of list may be valuable for helping someone cope in the community, but the expectation is still for non-recovery, given that the prevailing theme is an emphasis on preparing for the next crisis rather than getting on with your life. The importance placed on crisis planning can only be valid if it is considered as part of a transitional programme towards recovery, rather than the goal in its own right.

Central to the Basic Tasks Model is the assumption that professional intervention is both essential and desirable. Within mental health services those who are defining social and clinical recovery are professionals who are themselves victims of their own belief systems about illness. This means that the definitions used for recovery will be rooted in a medical model rather than in a personal and subjective framework.

Even within social recovery, this medicalisation is evident in the terminology used throughout the 'Basic Tasks in Recovery' framework listed above. Understanding the use of language is important if we are to understand the failure of the mental health system to achieve sustainable recovery on a large scale. The Basic Tasks framework is littered with the language of mental illness rather than the language of recovery: professional interventions, supports, medical care, medication, symptoms, assistance, treatment facilities, crisis, ongoing coping monitoring and responding strategies.

I have chosen to designate this methodology as one based on non-recovery because of the prominence placed on the notion of illness rather than wellness. Whilst it is true that many of the elements used by both Warner and Carling are important to the recovery process, it must be realised that both agendas have their foundations within the psychiatric system and are therefore based on the premise that 'illness' is a biological construct. This means that all interventions or techniques used by professionals will retain this biological causation as the focus of treatment and, by implication, as the focus of recovery.

Given that this is the case then surely the only conclusion that can be reached is that within psychiatry, social recovery is a myth and is used by professionals as a way of monitoring and ensuring compliance. It is in fact nothing more than a means to a dead end. Both Warner and Carling reinforce this view. For Warner, it is clear that it does not matter whether you measure clinical features (such as psychosis or anxiety) or social features (such as number of friends or sexual functioning): they both have an equal value in the measurement of recovery. The reality for the client is that social functioning is affected by the treatment they receive. Therefore there is a direct correlation between clinical and social recovery, though it is not the one that psychiatrists would have us believe.

Chapter Four

CONSTRUCTION, DECONSTRUCTION, AND RECONSTRUCTION

Power Or Empower: Is That the Question?

I am one of those who hold to the idea that the process of personal recovery has, at its very heart, the reclamation of personal power. In order for the journey of recovery to be successful I believe that it is important to deconstruct the power of the psychiatric system and to reconstruct power as a personal commodity.

The present psychiatric system is rooted almost entirely in the perceived power of the psychiatric professional. I use the term 'perceived power' rather than real power, because much of the power invested in psychiatric professionals does not intrinsically come from them, but is given by the state. This means that professional power is, in essence, politically based rather than knowledge- or practice-based. It also follows that the extent and level of professional power is under the control of politicians. The fact that the state has entrusted this power to the keeping of the psychiatric profession at the present time does not mean that this will always be the case.

Many of us have spent, and continue to spend, much of our time in trying to change the views of mental health professionals on the assumption that they have the power that creates, drives, and maintains the present system. This assumption is an assumption too far, for while there is no doubt that the professional administers the mental health system (and as a result makes choices for the patients within it) I doubt whether they have as much power as we seem to give them. The authority given to them by the state (their legal power) may still be too much, but it is nevertheless limited to the letter, if not the spirit, of the law. The bulk of their power comes not from the state but from the power ceded to them by carers, family, and service users.

Within any type of health system this ceding of power is a normal process. Consider what happens when you go to your General Practitioner. I may make an appointment due to a concern about my hearing, and will start by describing what the problem is (e.g. 'I am having trouble hearing in my left ear'). With these words I do two things. First, I expect her to find out what is wrong and resolve it. Second, I put myself in her hands. In other words, I give up personal autonomy (power). She may decide to refer me on to a specialist, and when I meet the specialist I will once again hand over my personal autonomy to a doctor. However, the expectation is that once the doctor has made his or her diagnoses and spoken to me about the available treatment options, he will allow me to reclaim my personal autonomy (power).

Like me, most people do not see a psychiatrist or a psychiatric professional until their teenage years or later, and by then our compliant response to the medical profession is well established. Our expectations for the psychiatric worker will be similar to the expectation we have of any other health professional, in that we will view our handing over of personal autonomy as a transitory thing. However, the reality for many is that psychiatric practice makes it almost impossible for us to reclaim our personal power.

Therefore one of the first hurdles we face in the recovery process is finding a way to take back power. The ongoing attempt to address the power imbalance within mental health has resulted in the creation of the notion of empowerment. Empowerment in general, and empowering users in particular, has become a form of political correctness within the mental health system. Unfortunately, however, it has not led to a change in practice, only a change in language, and in effect has failed to deliver autonomy to the service user. One of the reasons for the failure of the empowerment approach is its failure to understand one of the fundamental truths about power: that it is not given but taken. If we look at the history of campaigns for freedom or equality, we can see that it was the perceived threat to the establishment (those who wield power) that made the establishment cede power.

Women in the UK are a case in point: they *won* the vote, they were not merely given the vote. Historically, the role of the suffragettes in this fight for emancipation cannot be denied (though the establishment sometimes tries to do so). Women were jailed, forcibly fed, and died in the battle to win the vote. It was their sacrifice that forced the state to concede female suffrage. Similarly, gay men and lesbians had to fight to win the right to live a particular lifestyle. They demanded and took the right to live their lives as they saw fit, and they did this by 'coming out of the closet' and demanding acceptance. This was against the background of homosexuality being deemed a mental illness right into the early 1970s, and it was the sheer volume of those speaking out that forced the law to be changed. The twentieth century also saw numerous colonies claiming independence from their colonial masters. Many of these colonies had to fight bloody wars to achieve their independence. It was not so much that these countries were given freedom, rather that they took their freedom and the colonisers merely gave way to the inevitable. Intervoice (see Box 1) is a good example of how these principles of social movement and justice have been utilised in the case of voice hearing.

After applying the same civil rights philosophy to the power issues faced by those using mental health services, I have come to the conclusion that the reclamation of power is something that is essential in any recovery process. Taking or reclaiming power conflicts with the empowerment approach currently adopted by the system, yet this conflict does not mean in itself that the two approaches cannot work together. In fact I prefer to call the conflicts that exist between the two 'contradictions'. This viewpoint (contradictions rather than conflicts) allows us to analyse the issue of power using dialectical methodology, which in turn will allow us to explore these contradictions in a positive way.

The ideas surrounding the need to empower users are based on an admission by professionals that power is an issue. Yet the real problem is not in their acknowledgment of this, but in the fact that they focus the issue of power as one that has the service user at its core. It is here that their analysis is flawed, for it is not the professionals' role to give power to clients. Their role should be to renounce their power and influence over service users, and by doing so create the conditions in which service users can reclaim power for themselves. Likewise it is not the role of the service user to passively wait to be empowered, but to be active in taking back their personal power.

This is not (and will never be) an easy thing for professionals or service users to do, and the difficulties that users and workers face when dealing with the issues of renouncing power should not be underestimated. Due to the way mental health practice is organised, professionals are forced to work within a system that is based on defensive practice. Defensive practice, by its very nature, does not encourage any form of risk-taking. Rather it does the opposite and ensures that practice is conservative at best, and oppressive at its worst. Yet the no-risk strategy creates the no-recovery culture and leads to the very power struggle that all sides claim they wish to end. 'Take no risks' has become the new mantra of mental health services, and as long as this is the case, recovery will not be a realistic option for the many. In 1998, the Minister of State responsible for mental health in the UK led the chant of the new mantra at the National Mind conference when he stated that noncompliance was not an option within mental health. I believe that this statement denies many service users one of the fundamental requirements for recovery: the fundamental right of a citizen to make choices (see also Chapter Seven). The right to choose treatment or to refuse treatment must be the service user's. In the next two sections, I will further explore choice within the context of a recovery programme.

Box 1. The Hearing Voices Movement

Emancipating Voice Hearers:
The Example of Intervoice

The groundbreaking research of Romme and Escher (see Chapter Two) began an exploration of the voice hearing experience that continues to this day, not least through inspiring and establishing what is now referred to as the hearing voices movement, a philosophical and social faction in which networks of voice hearers develop ways to support one other, empower themselves and work towards recovery. It was also the beginning of another paradigm shift, in which the identity of the 'schizophrenic' receded and the newly defined 'voice hearer' emerged. While traditional psychiatry emphasises the eradication and suppression of voices, the hearing voices movement offers an alternative approach that values the voice hearing experience as meaningful, significant, and originating within the context of the person's life story. Through talking about voices and finding positive ways to communicate and relate to them, individuals can learn to give their voices a personal and positive meaning, cope with them effectively, and ultimately create a fulfilling life that the voices become part of.

Paul Baker (1989), who witnessed Romme and Escher publicly delivering their findings for the first time, later recorded:

'Fundamental to this approach ... has been its emphasis on partnership between voice hearers themselves and professionals ... this was a refreshing change from most of the approaches I had come across before which rarely, if ever, gave such importance to the views of those who had actually experienced the mental health difficulties under consideration.' (p.11)

Romme (2000) has since likened the emancipation of voice hearers to the Civil Rights movements of the 1960s, arguing that psychiatry must change its attitudes toward voice hearing in the same way it changed its attitudes towards homosexuality – by learning to respect and support rather than 'cure' it. Warwick (quoted in James, 2001) makes this political point explicitly:

'How much longer is psychiatry going ...[to continue] labelling first one thing, then another, as mental sickness? Look at the record of psychiatric blundering that has quietly been crossed off with no apologies, let alone any compensation for the many victims. Masturbation, homosexuality, having a child out of wedlock ... these are but a few of the many natural ways of human nature, that in Britain at least, no longer qualify for diabolical forms of treatment psychiatrists inflict upon those they are empowered to label mentally sick.' (p.41)

The hearing voices movement affirms this viewpoint, and the approach has become progressively more powerful and influential, dispersing across the world in the form of user-led networks, research, forums, conferences, publications, and self-help groups. There are now hearing voices networks in twenty-one countries, coordinated via Intervoice: The International Network for Training, Education and Research into Hearing Voices (www.intervoiceonline.org). Its supporters comprise a mixture of experts by profession and experts by experience, including: Paul Baker, Richard Bentall, Peter Bullimore, Hywell Davies, Jacqui Dillon, Eleanor Longden, Rufus May, Phil Thomas, and Rachel Waddingham (UK); Wilma Boevink, Dirk Corstens, Bernadine Ensink, Jim van Os, and Jeanette Woolthius (Holland); Yann Derobert (France); Michaela Amering (Austria); Gail Hornstein (USA); Monika Hoffman, Hannelore Klafki, and Caroline Von Taysen (Germany); Ami Rohintz and Alain Topor (Sweden); Marcello Marcario, Pino Pini, and Alessandra Santoni (Itay); Wakio Santoni (Japan); Gonzales de Chavez (Spain); Joe Calleja, Lyn Mahboub, and John Watkins (Australia); Debra Lampshire and John Read (New Zealand); and Jørn Eriksen, Trevor Eyles, Andrew Moskowitz , and Olga Runciman (Denmark).

The foundation of Intervoice has created opportunities for both acknowledging and supporting voice hearers, and spreading awareness that even extremely distressed people can be supported to reclaim control over their lives and live happily with their voices (see Romme, Escher, Dillon, Corstens, & Morris, 2009). Accepting and making sense of voices has therefore become a new paradigm, constructively creating new ways of recovery. Furthermore, emphasis is increasingly being given to the expertise of experience, with academic, clinical and professional knowledge bases collaborating with voice hearers themselves in ever more equitable ways.

The Role of the Self

In Chapter One, I provided an account of my own recovery process, which was based on a speech I gave in Maastricht in January 1999. At the end of the conference I was in a bar talking to some of the delegates, when one of them (who is a friend of mine) commented on the fact that he had enjoyed the first part of the speech, which was about people. He then went on to say that he had found the second part, about self, something of a contradiction given my political beliefs. In this section I intend to develop further the issues I raised in Chapter One by looking closely at my stepping stones to recovery, focusing on the issues of self and ownership.

If recovery is not to be viewed as a clinical construct then we must develop a different context in which the notion of recovery can be discussed. I have already contextualised recovery as personal, whereby it is the individual themselves who is best placed to define what recovery is. However this does not mean that recovery occurs in a vacuum, and that the individual goes it alone separated from society. Rather I believe that recovery is a liberating experience that occurs through the politicisation of the self within wider society. What we cannot get away from is the role that the self plays within the decision-making process.

Descartes defines the notion of self within his famous phrase, 'I think therefore I am.' I would contend, however, that self becomes clearer when the quote is amended to: 'I think therefore I am – I think'. The addition of these final words completes the contradiction of Descartes in understanding the role of self within society. The role of the self within recovery is much more difficult to define without appearing to fall into the trap of the heroic self.

It was this issue of the heroic self that created the problems for my friend. He felt that by emphasising the part played by self in the recovery process, then a danger existed that self would be glorified at the expense of the role that other people play within the individuals' recovery process. Throughout my career as a speaker, many professionals have approached me to tell me how brave I have been in facing my madness. Is this, then, the heroic self that my friend is talking about? For if it is, then the heroic self is a creation of others, not the self. If this is indeed the case, then the heroic self is not the real problem. Rather, the real problem is that of professional perception.

The four selves that I discuss in Chapter One (self-confidence, self-esteem, self-awareness, and self-acceptance) should not be interpreted as a route to recovery that is wholly conducted by the individual. Rather, the four selves can only be fully understood when they are considered in relationship to the individual's interactions with others. When we examine the four selves in detail, one realises the contradiction that exists in the notion of self: self cannot exist without others to validate its existence. Therefore one can argue that the emotional or psychological self cannot (indeed does not) exist in a vacuum. How can we understand self-esteem if we do not view it as an emotional and psychological response, recognisable both in ourselves and others, that is in constant change? How can we understand the notion of being self-confident if there were not periods in our lives when we lacked confidence and were helped to gain that confidence by others? Remember, for instance, the very first time we try something new, such as driving a car. We need to learn from the beginning, and normally we would have someone teaching us until we were confident enough to do the thing for ourselves. How do we develop self-awareness if it is not through interactions within human responsiveness? The idea that we can go and discover ourselves through being totally and enduringly solitary is a myth. We may only be aware of how much we love someone when we lose them, but we need to have loved them in the first place to be fully aware of the pain that love can bring when it is withdrawn. Accepting ourselves for what we are requires the same type of analysis of self: that is, understanding that interacting with other people is a prerequisite.

If self cannot exist in isolation (and if our understanding of self can only be defined in terms of interactions between the individual and others) then this would mean that self is actually comprised of a series of complex relationships with others which can only be measured by the emotional impact we have on other people, and the effect that they have on our emotions in their turn. Although at first glance this may seem an unimportant point in terms of a recovery process, closer inspection will hopefully show that the appreciation of this notion of self is essential in understanding recovery. To my mind, the questions that we need to address at this time are fairly simple, and revolve around whether the experience of self is altered by life events. If this is the case, are we dealing with mental illness or a crisis of the self as it relates to society?

The destruction of relationships can also be seen in traumatic life events. For example, whilst I was in hospital I met quite a few students who had their first psychotic breakdown during their freshman year at university. Most had left home for the first time and were living in halls of residence. They had left their family and friends and found it difficult to adjust to their new surroundings (bear in mind that moving home is considered the second most stressful life event after a death in the family). It was within this context that many of these students started to hear voices, to see things, or begin to believe things that others find hard to understand. The system saw these events as the onset of mental illness and treated the students accordingly. I believe it would have been more appropriate to view the breakdown as one of a dilution of their identity, caused by the breakdown of their relationships and removal from their hometowns.

From speaking with these students, it became clear that for most of them the psychosis, far from being a result of their biology, was a response to their sense of loneliness and alienation. Most of them stated that they felt they had lost their identity as a member of a family, leading them to withdraw from the college scene and into themselves. It was after they had withdrawn from their peers that the voices and other experiences occurred; much the same as with the lone yachtsmen who starts to experience voices within his isolation. Whilst it is difficult to claim that these students had suffered a destruction of self-identity, there can be no doubt that the isolation they endured had caused a dilution of self. This is reflected in their pervasive lack of self-confidence, self esteem, self-awareness, and self-acceptance. Indeed, researchers such as Kinderman and Bentall (1996), Romme and Escher (2000), and Birchwood et al. (2000) have commented on the role that self-esteem plays in the outcome of psychiatric patients. Others such as Beck-Sander (1999) have examined self-acceptance, whilst Fisher (1994) and Lawson (1994) note the importance of self-confidence and self-awareness in recovery. Dilution of the self is not, however, caused by internal factors. Rather it is external features (in the case of the students, leaving home and the resultant sense of isolation) which leads to the experience of such acute mental distress. Indeed, the experience of invalidation, maltreatment, and adversity, particularly (though not exclusively) childhood sexual abuse has been consistently shown as a major factor in the onset and maintenance of distressing voices, as well as a plethora of other mental health problems (e.g. Corstens et al., 2008; Gracie et al., 2007; Read et al., 2003; Read et al., 2005; Romme & Escher, 2010; Shevlin et al., 2007; Whitfield et al., 2005). Although experiences like voice hearing, unusual beliefs, and paranoia are prevalent in the general population – indeed, there are around sixteen times more people who hear voices than who receive treatment for psychosis (Romme, 2010) – trauma exposure appears to be a reliable way of distinguishing distressed from non-distressed voice hearers, wherein beliefs formed in response to trauma determine subsequent distress and incapacity (e.g. Andrew et al., 2008; Bak et al., 2005; Chisholm et al., 2006; Offen et al., 2003). Therefore, as stated previously, the students' sense of self cannot be understood without an insight into their relationships and experiences prior to leaving home and, in these cases, the lack of relationships on the college campus.

The insistence of many professionals on conceptualising strong emotions as part of a degenerative illness process means that 'my self' is generally perceived as damaged and in need of repair. Within such a system it is no wonder that many of us feel that our very identities have been destroyed. It also follows that the service providers' denial of self (as it is expressed through the individuals' experience or behaviour) will eventually lead the person to deny their experiences in order to keep the peace. In turn, this compliance allows the professional to claim a moral and scientific authority over both the individual and society as a whole.

In Chapter Three we discussed how this moral and scientific authority is based on poorly conceived and researched ideas around the definition of clinical and social recovery as they relate to mental ill health. This has meant that much of what we deem evidence-based practice is rooted in assumptions about causation and treatment effectiveness, rather than the reality of the experience as understood by the client. I would argue that, rather than the progression of a biological illness, it is the failure of professionals to understand the reality of a person's experience that causes their identity to be in danger of destruction. The real importance of the notion of self I am proposing is that madness, far from being an illness, is for many a desperate attempt to preserve the self.

Ownership

In addition to the concept of self, I have always placed great store by the idea of who has ownership over the experience of mental distress. This, like self, is a concept that can cause difficulty for some, in that (like self) it initially appears to exclude all except the individual from the process. As with self, first impressions are deceptive. My belief is that taking ownership of our experience is in essence a political and liberating process, and as such is essential to recovery. In this section I will explore the reasons that I hold this particular belief about ownership.

In Chapters One and Two, I argued that professionals, carers, friends, or lovers cannot own the client's experience: only the individual can own their experience. I continue here in the same vein, concluding that it is only through owning the experience that a person can own recovery. This is a statement I have made on many occasions without developing it any further, yet it is probably one of the most important issues that I talk about. I hope that readers will not consider my need to develop this theme too much of a self-indulgence, but rather as an opportunity to explore for themselves the implications of who owns a person's experience – and the importance of that ownership. Within the realms of psychiatric practice it is generally accepted that the most powerful practitioner is the psychiatrist. Their power is rooted not only in the authority given to them by the state, but also in their singular right to make diagnoses. It is this ownership of a supposed expert knowledge that gives them so much power over their clients. I would contend that the real expert in the client's experience is the client, and that it is not psychiatrists who own the knowledge that makes recovery possible.

The main problem that many people have with the construct of *ownership* is the connotations associated with the word. For some, it is seen as part of the Thatcherite cult of the individual, and as such has no place in the development of a collectivist or inclusion-based system. To me, however, this would only be a valid argument if the ownership of a person's experience was already a collectivist matter, and if the individual was attempting to create an individualistic approach from something that was already held in common ownership. Since this common ownership is not currently in existence, then the transitional phase must be the wresting of the ownership (1) from the professionals, (2) for the client, (3) by the client.

In some respects, there are a group of psychiatric patients who are the modern equivalent of the American black slaves in that they find their entire lives being owned by psychiatric professionals. 'Nonsense,' many will say; but let us look at the comparisons. In *The Politics of the Madhouse* (Coleman, 1998), I described the client as a commodity who was bidded for through a tendering process between agencies vying to provide care services. What concerned me was the tendering process as a method by which clients were alienated from both the system of care and the workers that provided the care. I now want to take this analysis further, my contention being that this tendering system can, in some cases, reduce clients to properties that are bought and sold in an open auction. This may appear incredible to the reader, but it is my recent experiences with the tendering system that have brought me to this conclusion.

Working in psychiatric services has meant that on the odd occasion I am involved in writing tenders, and it was during one such commission in May 1999 that I first started making comparisons with the slave trade. The tender involved moving people out of a nursing home that offered twenty-four-hour nursing care into the community, with varying degrees of support to be offered to the clients. I confess that I did not think very much about the people involved as I was writing my part of the tender. It was only when I was at the presentation to the purchasers that I realised there was a whole group of us talking about people as if they were property. What I mean by this is that the clients under discussion had no idea about what was going on. They would never be consulted about which agency would take over the provision of their care and their future. In effect they were being auctioned off, with the main priority being cost. There is no way that this approach of selling people can be justified as an ethical way of contracting services. The result of this particular tendering process was that the organisation that had been looking after the clients did not win the tender, and the clients were handed over to another provider without a second thought. Only when the auction was over were the clients informed that their lives were now to be organised by a new master. I am not saying that provider organisations involved in the tendering culture do not care for their clients. Nevertheless I believe that many organisations, whilst caring for their clients, simultaneously do nothing to prove that they really care about them. My view is that this type of tendering process (that which does not involve the service consumer in every aspect and at every stage) can offer little or no practical health gain for the client. Indeed, I believe that in many cases it will be actively detrimental to the recovery journey, because it devalues and dehumanises the individual in much the same way that slavery did.

It is not only in the auction room (tendering process) that similarities between slavery and patienthood exist. Clients who refuse to accept their diagnoses or the treatment offered are considered noncompliant, which is also considered as having a lack of insight. The doctor, via the state, can respond to this by forcibly treating the person. If the client decides to leave the hospital, it is not considered a rational decision, but (once again) part of their illness – and once again the doctor has the power to restrain them, or to have them forcibly returned to the hospital by the police. Compare this with the circumstances of the black slave. Once sold to a master, the slave was expected to accept his lot; failure to do so was deemed a sign of maladjustment. Non-acceptance was considered to show a lack of understanding by the slave of his condition in life: that is, a lack of insight. When the slave complained, or fought against their treatment, this was also seen as noncompliance and lack of insight. If slaves dared to escape, they were condemned as acting irrationally (indeed they were often seen as ill; the diagnosis was called drapetomania) and would be returned to their master by force.

There is a positive similarity between the slave and the psychiatric 'problem patient', in that while both groups could be bodily imprisoned within their respective systems, neither system could control the desire of the oppressed to be free. Indeed, both groups created their own freedom in the only place the system could never fully control them: their minds. Like the slave, freedom begins with the rejection of another's right to own you. Rejecting the ownership that others claim to have over your experience is to accept personal ownership of that experience. It is also the first step in taking power back from the system. A major consequence of not reclaiming ownership from the system can be the breaking down, and eventually the destruction, of the individual's self-identity. When this destruction is complete, the system has created yet another chronic patient. It was for this reason that I came to the conclusion that ownership, despite the political connotations, is an essential part of the recovery process.

In the next two chapters, it is my intention to take these elements (self and ownership) and add a further two components (choice and people) to create a simple programme of recovery.

Chapter Five

THE PROFESSIONAL AS AN AGENT OF RECOVERY

The focus of this book so far has been on the role of the client in the recovery process. In this chapter I will explore the role of the professional in the recovery process, both individually and as part of a team approach.

One of the big myths about the pre-neuroleptic psychiatric system is that people entered it and never came out. This clearly was not the case. Indeed, of those clients diagnosed as having schizophrenia fully one-third recovered and left the hospital (Bentall, 2004). It is my belief that this was due in no small measure to the interventions carried out by nursing staff. Most of these interventions would, in our present system, be called psychosocial interventions and be seen as the preserve of the clinical psychologist. Since the introduction of major tranquillisers in the mid-1950s, the professional role has changed from one of proaction to one of reaction (or, in many cases, inaction).

Nevertheless, there have always been groups of professionals who have sought to do things differently. Psychiatrists from the days of Carl Jung, through to R. D. Laing and Thomas Szasz, to those of today like Jan Dirk Blom, Pat Bracken, Dirk Corstens, Alec Jenner, David Kingdon, Joanna Moncrieff, Marius Romme, Phil Thomas, Douglas Turkington, and Jim van Os, who have striven tirelessly (often against mainstream thinking) to effect change in both attitudes and practice within the system. Individuals like Phil Barker, Poppy Buchanan-Barker, Paul Hammersley, Mervyn

Morris, Julie Repper, Mike Smith and Karen Taylor have all pushed recovery to the fore of the nurse's role. Psychologists such as Richard Bentall, Max Birchwood, Peter Chadwick, Gillian Haddock and Nicholas Tarrier have developed the use of cognitive forms of treatment for people with psychotic symptoms. Another group of psychologists has taken a political view of psychiatry, including Mary Boyle, Lucy Johnstone, Warren Larkin, Terry McLaughlin, Anthony Morrison, Ian Parker, John Read and Dorothy Rowe.

While I do not agree with the views of all of the above, it must be stated that they were, or are, doing something different, often in the face of opposition from other colleagues. Much of the present-day resistance to biomedical psychiatry has rooted itself in the theories developed by some of these professionals. For example, although now generally regarded as providing short-term relief, the coping strategy enhancement work of Tarrier and colleagues (e.g. Tarrier et al., 1993) was significant far beyond its benefits to the client group. The reason for this was that for the first time since Jung, an effective way of working psychologically with clients who were actively psychotic had been developed and tested. Similarly, researchers such as Haddock, Bentall and Slade (1996) via their focusing technique, and Birchwood and colleagues (e.g. Birchwood et al., 2000) through their early intervention programmes provided mainstream alternatives to biological accounts of psychosis and endorsed the development of psychological therapies previously denied to psychotic patients (British Psychological Society, 2000).

In contrast, the deconstructive approach of Parker and other critical psychologists added a new dimension through the provision of a political basis for service users to root their opposition to the system. For example, in *Deconstructing*

Psychopathology (Parker et al., 1995) the authors write:

> As we go through the book we show why it is necessary to 'deconstruct' psychopathology, and describe what we mean by 'practical deconstruction' ... As we unravel [and] deconstruct traditional notions ... we suggest strategies for change, and hope that you will be inspired into building [and] reconstructing something better. (p. viii)

It is within these strategies for change that I believe we can find real hope for the implementation of a recovery-driven psychiatric system. Although there is nothing new in the strategies suggested within the book, its importance for me is in the academic weight of the writers and its politicisation of the psychiatric system.

For example, McLaughlin's chapter on the development of the Hearing Voices Network (HVN) focuses on the importance of self-help in the recovery process. This chapter is a must for professionals who wish to set up hearing voices groups. More than this, it is a chapter of hope for those who are distressed by negative voices through providing a new way of dealing with these experiences. One of the great myths of HVN is that all the groups were set up and run by voice hearers. Running alongside this myth (and equally wrong) is the view that all groups were established and maintained by professionals. The truth, as is customary, lies somewhere in the middle: the groups were set up and run by both professionals and voice hearers. It is not my role to make any judgement about which method of setting up groups is best. Rather in this section I will explore how professionals can enable such groups to develop in a way that facilitates recovery.

Many of the professionals I have spoken to who have set up hearing voices groups have told me that one of the main things that struck them on a personal level was the amount of time it takes. They had begun the groups thinking that it would meet once a week for an hour or two, and that after each meeting it would be over until the next week. They soon discovered that nothing could be further from the truth, and far from the group taking up an hour or two each week, it would very quickly consume an entire day or two of their time. I consider this process to be a very natural one, as what often happens in these type of self-help groups is that the members bond very quickly and the group becomes more than just a place where people talk about their voices (or self-harm, or unusual beliefs, or whatever it is the group is concerned with). For many clients, groups are a place where lives are shared, a place where pain and distress is disclosed to such an extent that there have been groups I have attended where the pain and distress has been almost tangible, almost solid, and very real. The idea that professionals can remain an objective observer in such situations is rendered nonsensical. Professionals, after all, arc human.

There is no doubt that workers involved in self-help groups find themselves changing as the group develops. One of them told me he felt as though the group had become part of his personal recovery. This was not a recovery from illness, but the recovery of his personal identity over his professional identity. He told me that for the first time in recent memory he felt he was doing what he had been trained to do. When I asked him to clarify this further, he told me that when he had entered the nursing profession he had thought that his work would involve healing people. Until the voices self-help group the reality had been somewhat different. He went on to describe how the real buzz for him was that as a practitioner he was now proactive in the recovery process. The other important thing for him was that he believed the voice hearers had begun to take control over their lives through the self-help group. For him, this meant that those members in the group who were also in his caseload had started on what he called the 'discharge road'. Indeed, within a year of the group starting he saw clients in the group being discharged from the system. He is now committed to staying in his profession and not leaving, as he had planned to do prior to his involvement in setting up the group.

Since 1992 I have had the good fortune to be involved in the setting up of hearing voices groups both in the UK and abroad, and in many cases I have been invited to visit an area by professionals who were keen to see self-help groups established. These workers often wanted to help set a group up, then withdraw and leave the voice hearers to get on with it. In my experience this withdrawal process takes much longer than is originally planned for (not due to the professionals wanting to hold onto the group, but because the voice hearers want the professionals to remain as part of it). I visited one such group in England in 1998, and again almost exactly one year later. Its membership (including the professional facilitating it) had remained almost the same since my first visit. What had changed were the people in the group. The majority of these were considered as 'chronic patients'. Many professionals had written them off as hopeless cases, and their futures were defined in terms of long-term care.

What a difference a year can make. Whereas on my first visit the members of the group said little (and in many cases nothing), now they were all talking. And they were not just talking about general things, they were talking about their voices and other experiences that had led them into the psychiatric system. They were also describing how they managed their experiences, and encouraging each other to try different coping strategies. One thing that they all identified as central to the group's success was its consistency – not only of the voice hearers attending, but the fact that the same professional had been part of the group since the beginning. As far as the members were concerned, the professional held an enabling function in that he was able to answer many of the clinical questions that they might have, and could provide information on such subjects as diagnoses, medication side effects, and different treatment options. The professional told me that the group was both challenging and rewarding and had changed many of the members' perspectives on what was happening to them. It had also changed his perspective of his role by shifting the focus from caring for a person to caring about the person. Though none of the members were ready for discharge, there was no doubt that they had progressed a long way on the recovery continuum. The professional's role within the group had been pivotal in this, and he could indeed be described as an agent of recovery.

As this example partially illustrates, recovery-orientated practice will only shift from rhetoric to reality by acknowledging the importance of our own recovery at a professional level. Karen Taylor, who describes herself as 'a recovering psychiatric nurse', identifies several strategies that can be used to implement recovery for both worker and workforce (see Box 2).

Box 2. Recovery for the Worker and the Workforce

Karen Taylor (RGN) states that there are several things professionals can do to ensure that recovery becomes a reality. These are:

1. Recognising the importance of story: when taking life histories, we stop listening after a while because all we're looking for are clues that will fit our diagnosis.
2. Changing our way of viewing risk: informed risk-taking rather than risk-aversion.
3. Acknowledging that, as workers, we have our own lived experience and we can use this in our practice.
4. Mirroring and modelling recovery through working in person-centred ways with both our coworkers and our clients.
5. Recognising that relationships are the key to effective recovery practice.
6. Showing our feelings and not hiding them under the guise of professionalism.
7. Practicing through freedom, not fear.

A Team Approach to Time Management

How many times have you heard professionals say that the biggest problem they have is the size of their caseload, and because of this they lack the time to deliver the quality of service they feel their clients deserve? Like many others, I believe that the answer to this problem must be a sizeable reduction in the caseloads carried by professionals. I would argue that for a worker to be fully effective, a caseload should be restricted to eight clients. This would mean that each client would have a half-day and the professional would have a whole day for meetings and paperwork. Unfortunately such a shift in method is unlikely to happen in the present climate. We therefore need to find other ways of creating quality time for clients.

Making Recovery a Reality, a recovery programme developed by Coleman and Smith (see Carling et al., 1999; Coleman & Taylor, 2007) is one attempt to resolve this problem through engaging clients and professionals on a recovery journey. The programme is simple to use and has its roots in the notion that recovery is a developmental process, that all clients are on the recovery continuum, and that professionals can facilitate the client's move along the continuum towards discharge (recovery). The aim of the programme is to work with teams in developing the practical skills necessary to facilitate recovery. It requires the team to start a full review and reassessment of all clients, which is then used to place the client into one of three following groups: (1) those who have both the potential, and the desire or motivation to recover; (2) those who have the potential but lack the confidence, desire or motivation to recover; and (3) those who, for various reasons, have been viewed as having no hope by the system. Once clients have been assigned to a group, the next task is to complete a Personal Development Plan with each client, which would closely examine areas of the client's experience that have yet to be resolved (see Chapter Seven). For example, if during the review it was found that a client was hearing persistent negative voices, then part of the plan might be to support them to cope better with the experience. In this scenario, the team would employ various tools, such as the Maastricht Interview Schedule (Romme & Escher, 2000), the *Working With Voices* workbook (Coleman & Smith, 2006), and a hearing voices self-help group. The same types of interventions would be applied to problems such as self-harm, alternative beliefs, visions, and other experiences.

On the face of it, it appears as if all that this would accomplish would be to increase the team's workload even further, and this would certainly be the case if workers thought they had to organise all of these things themselves. However, if we look at how this could be implemented then a different picture emerges. The idea behind distributing the clients into the three groups is twofold:

1. To fast-track as many clients out of the system as quickly as possible. Though this may appear to favour the clients in Group One, in the medium term it will in actual fact benefit all clients, since much of the work with Group One can be done as a group. This will save time in that clients will be seen by the professional regularly and if there is a need for a one-to-one meeting it can be arranged at this time.

2. To enable the remaining clients to enter the fast-track process through facilitating the implementation of their personal recovery plans. Once again, much of this work can be done in groups. Indeed, the aim is to encourage this group to be in the same group meetings as those in the fast-track. This method is commonly called peer support in research papers, although I prefer the term self-help.

This programme not only develops clients' recovery potential, but also has been designed to develop the team's practical skills through ongoing training. These training needs are identified via client recovery plans, in that as each plan is completed, the team identify what skills they lack which would be required to work with the client. When the needs of the team have been identified, workers will be given the appropriate training to meet these needs. The other area that the teams are encouraged to develop is their team meetings. Instead of using them to discuss all of the clients briefly, they are encouraged to focus on only one or two clients who may be having a difficult time. The rationale behind this is simple: focusing on one or two clients allows the team time to explore different possibilities for these clients in much greater depth than would normally be possible in a team meeting. I am always amazed at the ideas that are generated by teams when they try this approach.

As you can see, all we have done in this programme is to combine a number of currently existing practices and give them equal validity within one team. This also means that the division between different professions becomes diluted, as groups of workers operating in this way will have all of the elements of a good multi-disciplinary team. In one of the services I work with, we have nursing staff, psychologists, occupational therapists, support workers, peer workers and medics all operating as equals, doing what is needed when it is needed. When all of these elements are working together using the same plan with the individual, then recovery becomes a reality.

Chapter Six

ORGANISATIONS AS
VEHICLES OF RECOVERY

*Building a true recovery system is as revolutionary a vision
as is building a criminal justice system based on forgiveness
instead of punishment, or creating an education system based
on love for learning instead of obedience to authority. We
may have to implement our vision in small increments.
Progress may be slow.*

Ragins, 2002

As stated earlier, the notion of recovery is nothing new within
the mainstream of psychiatric thinking. Indeed, the whole
of the second part of *Anatomy of Melancholy* (Burton,
1621/2001), some 500 pages, are devoted to recovery from
melancholy in its various forms:

> Inveterate Melancholy however it may seem to be
> a continuate inexorable disease, hard to be cured
> ... yet many times it may be helped, even that
> which is most violent. (p. 219)

Even in the old English language of the seventeenth
century, the idea of recovery from mental turmoil is at the
very least recognised and, in my opinion, also practiced. In
the eighteenth century the York Retreat (1796) opened and
with it the beginning of a moral treatment regime that can
still be seen in some of the rehabilitation services currently
operating. Furthermore, nursing textbooks in the 1960s were
clear that one of the roles of the nurse was to encourage

clients through the rehabilitation and recovery process (Boyd & Nihart, 1998).

Historically, then, there is little doubt that the underlying desire for recovery has been (and remains) a concept espoused in the statutory sector. It is also clear that, at least historically, psychiatry's role was not confined to treating only a disease of the brain, but to a much wider view of a person's ability to function within an insane society.

The idea that medical intervention can in some magical way be separated from the other elements of recovery is therefore a nonsense that can no longer be allowed to continue. Instead, we need to promote the diversity of the recovery experience, acknowledging as we do so the expertise of the client as the primary author of their own recovery journey. There is no need for psychiatry to be in defensive mode – far from it. The available evidence demonstrates that clients are clear about the importance of effective professional intervention in their recovery journeys (Liberman & Kopelowicz, 2002; Liberman et al., 2002). Clients with a diagnosis of schizophrenia pointed to a number of interventions that were part of their personal recovery experience. These included supportive therapy (positive relationships with psychiatrists, therapists, and other treatment teams created hope and appeared essential to improvement, with 78% of clients citing accessible and supportive psychiatrists and therapists as contributing to their recovery) and access to care (continuous, comprehensive treatment was also identified as crucial to recovery, including medication and psychotherapy, social skills training, family participation, vocational rehabilitation, and self-help groups).

Dr Robert Lieberman (2002), the lead author of the research, concluded that:

> Our findings join a growing body of research
> that flies in the face of the long-held notion that
> individuals diagnosed with schizophrenia are
> doomed to a life of disability with little expectation
> for productive involvement in society, a fatalistic
> view that in itself is damaging to prospects for
> recovery. By understanding the dynamics of recovery,
> we can design more effective courses of treatment
> and combat the pessimism held by many doctors,
> patients, and families struggling to cope. (p. 1)

Mark Ragins is a psychiatrist working in The Village
Integrated Service Agency, a program of the Mental Health
Association in Los Angeles County, California. This program
has evolved into a recovery-based service that puts the client
at the centre of the process. Ragins (2002) himself describes
his journey towards working in a recovery-orientated way as
a life-changing process that challenged much of the perceived
wisdom he had been taught as a young doctor. One of the
biggest challenges he faced was in the whole area of assessment,
where he believed that traditional methods not only failed the
client but were also failing the professional. He writes:

> Before we, as mental health professionals, can help
> people form visions for their future, we need to
> know them as people and not just as diagnoses. Our
> objective assessment of the signs and symptoms of
> their illness will not help them imagine recovery
> in their future. As John Strauss at Yale urges, we
> need to do a subjective assessment, which is similar
> to the assessment an actor does when he tries to
> get into a role and understand the character's
> inspirations and motivations. In order to do this

type of assessment, the professional needs to get emotionally inside the skin of someone with a serious mental illness, and that type of empathetic connection frightens many of us. (p. 14)

Can it be that this fear of empathy is the very thing that is stopping the recovery culture being embraced throughout the statutory sector? As a mental health professional, I feel obligated to understand my clients' experiences so that I might understand not only them as people, but what might be helpful to them in their recovery journey. However, I do not believe that they should be obligated to understand my service world with its rules, protocols, and clinical jargon in order to receive help from me.

Ragins tells a wonderful story that illustrates the problem that professionals face when trying to understand clients:

Bill, a man in his early 30s who has schizophrenia, came into my office late one afternoon. He held up his hand with his palm facing me and asked, 'What do you see?' I was tired and answered unenthusiastically, 'Your hand.' This didn't satisfy Bill. He said, 'No, no. Be more specific. What do you see?' I said, 'Okay, I see the swirls of your fingerprints, the creases where your fingers bend, and those lines that are your love line and life line.' Pointing from his eyes to the back of his hand, he said, 'When you can see nails and knuckles and hair, then you'll be able to help me because you'll be seeing the world from my side instead of yours.' (Ibid, p. 15)

Understanding the world from the clients' point of

view does not require all professionals to become patients in order to see clearly. Rather it requires professionals to remain in touch with their own humanity, especially when in contact with clients: to see beyond the symptoms, beyond the behaviour, beyond the patient, beyond themselves indeed, to see the person beyond their illness. This understanding can and does exist within statutory services, and many professionals do see the person beyond their illness. Why are we surprised then when we hear workers in the statutory sector talk about recovery within their services? Perhaps the problem here is not the statutory sector and its perceived inability to deliver recovery-based services, but the rest of us and our inability to accept that some in the statutory sector both believe in the process of recovery and deliver recovery-orientated services.

Though much still remains to be done there is no doubt that recovery has arrived within the statutory sector and it is now a matter of building on what has already begun. Much of this building will need to focus on the implementation of person-centred planning as a tool to achieve recovery outcomes and the introduction of a value base that will inform the process of recovery (see Chapter Seven).

No matter whether we work in the statutory, voluntary, or the independent sector there will be a common process that will underpin recovery-orientated services. Over the last few years we have called this the recovery process.

Let us return once again to Ragins. In one of his papers, he discusses the role of interventions in the recovery process:

> When I ask Village members what the staff did that was the most helpful, they never say, 'It was that clever combination of Resperidone, Depakote and Serzone you prescribed.' They always recall

some moment of human kindness or a time when
we believed in them. They recall the moment when
our walls were down or when we were genuinely
happy for them or even when we cried. We helped
them when we were real. That's when they could
tell we had hope. (Ibid, p. 15)

Recovery offers a new energising vision for people with
mental illness, their families and the professionals who serve
them. The momentum is already building but, so far, the
philosophy and values of recovery are only practiced in
isolated pockets across the country. The mental health system,
as a whole, is far from being recovery-based. Government
funding mechanisms are still mired in a medical necessity
model that rewards symptoms and illness and discourages
innovation or different ways of working. Even if we can't
change the entire mental health system, there are things we
can do in our existing mental health practices and programs
that will promote recovery.

Developing Recovery Practice

If recovery is to become a reality, then organisations need to
become vehicles of the recovery process. This requires both a
change in the mindset of organisations, and the development
of a recovery platform that is value-based (see also Chapter
Seven). However, organisations being what they are, they
must be persuaded that it is in their best interests to make
the move to recovery-orientated services before they will
actually do so.

Helen Glover (2001) in her discussion paper *Uncovering
Recovery* emphasises that recovery values are not the sole
province of distressed individuals, but are the concern and

responsibility of multiple stakeholders at various levels, including:

1. Policy makers
2. Commissioners
3. Organisations that provide services
4. Practitioners
5. Those that use services
6. Those that play a significant role in the lives of people who experience mental illness/distress
7. The general community at large

While the interplay between these stakeholders appears hierarchical, it must be remembered that all players have a responsibility to look seriously at their role within recovery-orientated service development and delivery.

This developing discussion is intended to facilitate an understanding of recovery-orientated service delivery. It helps us to recognise how all stakeholders can interplay to provide what we understand as recovery practices. It also attempts to provide a value base for which recovery practice can be developed and delivered.

In contrast, Spaniol (2001) identifies the following values that support the development and delivery of recovery-orientated services:

RECOVERY VALUE	DESCRIPTION
Empowerment	Creating a personal vision and having the confidence to move toward it. Feeling 'I can' versus 'I can't'
Personal choice	People know how to lead their life better than someone else does
Personal involvement	Participating in the processes by which decisions are made that affect one's life

RECOVERY VALUE	DESCRIPTION
Community focus	Building on existing resources in the community
Focus on strengths	Building on existing strengths in the person
Connectedness	Enhancing relationship to self, others, environments, meaning/purpose

Consider the rationale for recovery-based services presented below in Box 3. Can we imagine our mental health services making the changes required to implement a system that adopts these elements? For many of us, the answer will be no: but does this mean we should just give up and go home? Again, I would argue that the answer to this question is no. Rather than give up, we should start looking at each of these twenty criteria provided by Glover (2001) and seek to find ways in which they can be implemented in our own individual practice, as well as within our organisations. Let us explore these reasons individually and look at what is already being done, as well as what could be done individually and organisationally to change the current ways of working.

Box 3. Reasons to Adopt and Develop Recovery Practice (adapted from Glover, 2001)

1. Services will be responsive to the needs of people with mental illness/distress

2. Services, in being responsive, will be effective and efficient

3. Services will have staff who feel valued and supported in their work

4. Services will have staff who feel fulfilled in their work with people with mental illness/distress

5. Service users will feel actively involved in their care

97

6. Service users will inform and be fully informed on all issues pertaining to their recovery

7. As planning is central to recovery practice, service users, significant others, and service providers will have prepared for contingencies and crises

8. Recovery practice is forward- and future-focused

9. Service users, their significant others and service providers will develop collaborative partnerships in their work towards recovery

10. Coercion and control of people's actions will not dominate practice

11. Evidence-based knowledge and value-based knowledge will coexist

12. An articulated value base will underpin each service's/ organisation's practice

13. Feedback will not be feared, but sought and embraced in the continual development of responsive and accessible services

14. Partnerships between all key stakeholders, including community members and groups, will be active and visible

15. People will move beyond the need for intensive service delivery

16. Service users will be educated about recovery processes and the applicability to their lives

17. The diversity of knowledge, experience and values of all stake-holders will be upheld

18. Within a recovery framework, providing diagnosis and prognosis is secondary to developing meaning and understanding

19. Inviting people to create a society where inclusion is a reality, and develop meaning to what is happening for them

20. A relationship based on equality where the mutuality of knowledge and experience is respected is more aligned with recovery relationships and outcomes

1. Services will be responsive to the needs of people with mental illness/distress. In all of the organisations I have worked for or visited, staff would say that they are responsive to people's needs in times of mental turmoil. Yet I would have to disagree with them, because I believe that in far too many cases, rather than being responsive to people's needs, what we are actually doing is being reactive to people's behaviours. As stated earlier in this book, our current system is very good at reactive working. Being responsive requires us to be proactive. Being responsive, or proactive, will not always mean keeping a person out of hospital, but it might mean making the process of hospitalisation a different experience for the client. One example of how this can be achieved occurred when I was working with a team in the West Midlands. We were asked to visit a client who was known to the service, and who was experiencing considerable distress. In fact this had reached the point that it was decided he should come into hospital. This had happened on numerous occasions in the past, and the process had normally been a Mental Health Act assessment that would decide he needed admitting (something he was loath to do and would refuse to do, which in turn meant a number of police would arrive and forcibly take him, whereby he would try to run away and end up being transferred to the locked ward). As a team we decided to try to do something different that would help break this cycle. Three of us (myself and two nurses) visited him at home, where it became obvious to us that he was in crisis and flitting from personality to personality every few minutes (he had a diagnosis of dissociative identity disorder). However, we decided that waiting for a Mental Health Act assessment would not change anything for him, so we agreed to try and negotiate with each of the personalities as they appeared with a view to a voluntary admission. One of his personalities decided he would like us to join him for a picnic, so one of the nurses went to the local shop and bought some food, which we ate on the floor of his living room. We spent the next three hours negotiating the hospital admission, not only with the client, but also with the consultant and the ward staff. For the first time in his life as a patient, he agreed to come into the ward on a voluntary basis. When we arrived at the unit the consultant was waiting, and we had a meeting between the client, the ward team, and our team, in which we discussed the plan for working with him. This was a clear example of responding to a crisis in a different way. Although we had not prevented the crisis becoming an admission, we had broken the previous pattern, and were able to work with the man in a much more proactive way.

2. Services, in being responsive, will be effective and efficient. As can be seen from the above example, this was a more effective and efficient way of working. I would argue that what we were able to do was create a therapeutic alliance with the client that was very different from the conflict-based relationship that had previously existed. This in turn had a knock-on effect in that treatment became subject to negotiation and discussion rather than compulsion. And this of course meant that as a team we were working with the person rather than on the person. Clearly this is much more efficient and effective. The major benefit for our team in this situation was that for many of us we felt as though we were doing our real jobs for the first time: in some cases for many years.

3. Services will have staff that feel valued and supported in their work. One of the reasons we were able to work with this client was the position taken by senior management and the consultant psychiatrist on the subject of recovery. Our NHS Trust as an organisation had decided that they would adopt a recovery-based approach to service delivery, and because the consultant involved also believed in this approach she was prepared to take risks and support the team in taking these risks. She was not the type of psychiatrist to immediately take recourse in medication or the Mental Health Act in order to feel secure in her job. Rather, she believed in discussion and reaching agreement with all those involved, and in doing so she effectively encouraged and supported staff, clients, and carers. This in turn meant the staff felt that their views were heard and that they felt valued as workers.

4. Services will have staff that feel fulfilled in their work with people with mental illness/distress. Once again the above story illustrates the fact that by working in a recovery-based way staff, as well as clients, can derive great benefits. In the three years that I worked with this team I was aware of only two members of staff moving on, and they went on to manage new teams being set up within the Trust. It is clear to me that where workers feel fulfilled in their roles then staff retention rates will be higher, with the added bonus of having not only a settled team but a client group that is much more secure and clear about the response they will receive from the service.

5. Service users will feel actively involved in their care. This seems such an obvious point that I almost left it out, yet my own experience of services should have made me realise that this is one of the areas in service delivery that we are still failing to get right. Far from being an active process, a service user's involvement in their care often remains one that is either nonexistent or extremely passive. In order for this to change, we need to move towards methods of planning that put the client at the centre of the process (see Chapter Seven). The use of person-centred planning methodology is not new in health care; it is an established approach within learning disabilities and it now needs to be implemented in mental health. It is my contention that failure to properly introduce person-centred planning methods will not only prevent users from being involved in their care, but will make recovery as a goal almost impossible to achieve.

6. Service users will inform and be fully informed on all issues pertaining to their recovery. Mike Smith, speaking at a conference in Birmingham in 1999, stated that: 'information and knowledge are power.' I fully agree with this statement, and believe that for too long services have used knowledge and information in a negative way. If services were to adopt the principle of being informed by their clients, and in turn giving proper information to their clients, then the difference to the quality of the relationship between service provider and service recipient would be positive for both sides. A good example of this is around the issue of medication and the side effects of medication. If services told clients what the known side effects of their medication was, and educated and supported them about the nature of their medication regimes, then the rate of noncompliance would drop significantly (e.g. Fleischhacker et al., 1994). It therefore makes sense for services to buy into the notion of giving clients full information about all aspects of their care. And in turn, this information must be informed and developed through consultation with clients.

7. As planning is central to recovery practice, service users, significant others, and service providers will have

prepared for contingencies and crises. It is essential that service providers and users prepare in advance for any crisis that may occur. Doing this recognises a number of important factors within a recovery platform. These include the fact that recovery does not mean the absence of symptoms (rather it is about getting on with your life despite them) and that a crisis does not inevitably need to result in a hospital admission and a return to being a full-time patient. Indeed, this can be avoided more often than not if good crisis resolution planning has been carried out. Though it is not possible to see into the future with our clients, it is possible to ensure that we develop strategies to deal with known triggers and historical responses to them.

8. **Recovery practice is forward and future-focused.** If recovery is to become a reality then providers need to move away from maintaining the status quo, in which clients' past histories determine the planning process, towards one in which the desires, dreams and aspirations of our clients are at the centre of the process (see Chapter Seven). Making this change would mean that hope would become a feature of service provision.

9. **Service users, their significant others and service providers will develop collaborative partnerships in their work towards recovery.** Services and organisations that are rooted in recovery should be active in developing collaborative working relationships with all stakeholders (including the wider community). Developing these types of relationships will create a climate in which recovery is seen as the expected outcome for those with mental health problems. This in turn would clearly impact on how people with mental health problems are perceived by the wider

community, and consequently help in the ongoing battle against discrimination and stigma.

10. Coercion and control of people's actions will not dominate practice. Any service rooted in recovery would find it inconceivable that one of its primary roles was the use of force (or even the threat of force) as a means of ensuring compliance. Conversely good recovery practice has negotiation and discussion at its core, seeking to find agreement through a collaborative approach to service provision rather than conflict through a domineering, macho approach. The use of any mental health legislation should become a last resort that is only utilised after all other approaches have been exhausted. Even in cases where the law is used, the duration of coercion should be kept to a minimum. Furthermore, seeking an agreed resolution must be a priority in cases where there is conflict between professionals and users, as failure to do this must surely hinder the recovery process.

11. Evidence-based knowledge and value-based knowledge will coexist. In my opinion the current obsession with evidence-based practice (and the exclusion of almost any other way of thinking about service provision) has diluted the development of new skills within services. The biggest asset any professional will accrue as they develop their own practice is a knowledge base gained through experience. If alongside a good knowledge base we add a clear value base then the impact for the client can only be a positive one.

12. An articulated value base will underpin each service's/ organisation's practice. It is all very well to have a value base that is theoretically good, but if the theory is not translated to practice then it is worthless. For an organisation to adopt recovery practice, it must also adopt recovery values (such as believing in the client's capacity to recover, accepting that clients are real experts in terms of their experience, and taking considered risks). Without these types of values then recovery will simply be another buzzword that will pass into the annals of history.

13. Feedback will not be feared, but sought and embraced in the continual development of responsive and accessible services. Although most services claim to embrace user involvement, a major complaint from user groups is that in reality this is not the case. Services operating in a recovery-based way will not fear feedback from clients, carers, and others involved (including their own staff). Rather they would view feedback as an opportunity to ensure that their services made changes as and when they were needed. Successful services would actively seek constructive criticism to enable them to remain both responsive and accessible to their clients.

14. Partnerships between all key stakeholders, including community members and groups, will be active and visible. All too often in our present system, the concept of partnerships is tokenistic. If services are to truly operate in partnership with all stakeholders then they must move towards having memorandums of understanding with stakeholders. This would put relationships between the main service provider and others on a formal footing, and away from the informal (often toothless) relationships that are currently in operation. While this would doubtless create tension between the provider and others, I for one believe that this would be a healthy tension.

15. People will move beyond the need for intensive service delivery. Services that operate on the basis of a recovery methodology would, over a period of time, move people out of the 'revolving door mentality' with interventions designed to kick-start the recovery journey. Too many clients find themselves in services for life, and too many services are designed in a way that allows this to happen. Recovery-based services should have clear exit pathways for clients: and not into other mental health services, but back to primary care. Essentially, the role of the mental health professional should simply be to make themselves redundant in their clients' lives.

16. Service users will be educated about recovery processes and the applicability to their lives. Much has been made about psychosocial education for clients in which they are taught to recognise their triggers and detect the onset of symptoms. We even teach clients about their diagnoses, so it would seem sensible to teach clients about the process of recovery and how to apply the process to their own lives.

17. The diversity of knowledge, experience, and values of all stakeholders will be upheld. It is sad that in a society as diverse as ours we need to address this issue at all, and it is perhaps the worst indictment of our present mental health system that there is still a lack of respect for different points of view. This can best be seen in the continuing dominance of the medical model of mental illness, which despite the growing weight of evidence finds itself becoming ever more entrenched in its search for biological and genetic explanations for mental 'illness'. A recovery approach would demand a shift away from the dominance of the medical model towards the adoption of a holistic model of health care. Acceptance of a holistic approach to mental health would allow all stakeholders, including the medical profession, to participate in the recovery process as partners.

18. **Within a recovery framework, providing diagnosis and prognosis is secondary to developing meaning and understanding.** In their seminal book *Accepting Voices*, Romme and Escher (1993) demonstrated that some 70% of voice hearers could locate their voice hearing experience within their lived experience. Romme and Escher's work is responsible for enabling many a recovery journey by promoting the view that psychosis can be understood as a normal response to abnormal events. If services are to deliver the goods on recovery, then much more time must be spent understanding the context of a person's experience, and much less time on trying to make sense out of the medical professions' understanding of the person's experience.

19. **Inviting people to create a society where inclusion is a reality, and develop meaning to what is happening for them.** Even if we convinced every service provider, every worker, and every service user that recovery is the way forward, it could end up counting for nothing if we fail to convince the wider community that recovery from mental health problems is not only to be desired, it can be the reality for many. This may mean that we need to see ourselves as not only agents for recovery with our clients, but also as agents for recovery within our wider society.

20. **A relationship based on equality where the mutuality of knowledge and experience is both respected and is more aligned with recovery relationships and outcomes.** Last but not least, we return to the relationship between worker and client. It is my opinion that this relationship is often a mirror image of the relationship between workers and management: if management do not have high expectations of their workforce, then it often follows that workers will not

have high expectations for their clients. I am not saying that individual workers would conduct themselves differently, but rather that if there is a prevailing culture of maintenance within an organisation then the culture itself will self-perpetuate and make the implementation of a recovery platform virtually impossible. Changing the culture to one of recovery demands that we accept as the essential expertise of all parties in creating services that deliver recovery outcomes.

Although getting organizations to work towards recovery outcomes for clients may seem a daunting and difficult task, it is nevertheless my belief that a failure to advance this approach will not only impede recovery for clients, it will impede the recovery of psychiatry as a health-orientated service and keep it as an illness-dominated institution. Moving away from a maintenance approach towards a recovery process is therefore essential if organizations are to provide services that are compatible with the desire of professionals, users, carers, and wider society to see effective and proactive systems that strive towards recovery in our communities.

Recovery and the Statutory Sector: Reclaiming the Role

To me, the defensive position taken by the system every time one attempts to critique any part of its theory, value base, or practice, is a clear indication of a system in crisis. Indeed, a common response to such criticism is to accuse those making it of being anti-psychiatry, or ill-informed, and there appears to be little attempt to engage in constructive dialogue (though I am sure that this dialogue goes on within the system itself). I believe it is time to explore the difficult questions that we must face in the future if we are to deliver recovery-orientated services in mental health. For example, when delivering recovery training, I am frequently asked the following questions:

1. What would the role of psychiatrists be if we started working in a recovery-based way?

2. Where is the evidence base for this type of practice?

3. What about the clients who do not want to recover?

I believe that these questions are easily answered on a surface level:

1. The role of the psychiatrist should be that of consultancy and diagnostics rather than case management (or indeed, team management).

2. There is a growing body of evidence for recovery as a theory, a practice, and an outcome – and that the evidence is easily found via a literature search.

3. The real problem is how we work with learned helplessness and institutionalisation, which in my opinion de-motivates clients and makes recovery seem unachievable.

However, these questions can also be explored in a much deeper way: indeed, in ways that could challenge the role of the system itself, firstly through the manner in which it creates a patient, and secondly in how it maintains the patient in the illness role.

The role of the psychiatrist is primarily to understand what is happening to the client. This is normally done through an assessment process, which through time will lead to a diagnoses being made. The diagnostic process involves using the categories of mental illness either in DSM-IV or in ICD-10. That these categories are considered evidence-based is now a point of great contention. This is especially true when we look at schizophrenia:

> It would seem that schizophrenia is an illness that consists of no particular symptoms, that has no particular outcome, and that responds to no particular treatment. No wonder research revealed that it has no particular cause. (Bentall, 2004, p. 87)

As we know, many claims have been made pertaining to the presence of specific disease markers in schizophrenia. Heinrichs (2001) conducted a Medline search for publications appearing between 1980 and 1999 that investigated these markers. After calculating the effect size for each study, Heinrichs concluded that:

> This extensive appraisal across many areas of neuroscience reveals no common abnormality in all cases of schizophrenic illness. The strongest, most consistent evidence suggests that 50–70% of schizophrenics are deficient in cognitive brain function. In comparison most of the neurobiological abnormalities in the illness probably occur in a minority of patients. Moreover close to 40% of the biological findings are so weak and variable that they may represent minor, unimportant, or chance abnormalities with no intrinsic link to schizophrenia. (p. 84)

The psychiatrist Dirk Jan Blom (2003), who studied the literature concerning the validity problem of schizophrenia for his PhD, therefore says: 'From the work of Heinrichs we may cautiously conclude that contemporary neuroscience research ... fails to provide persuasive means of validation for the schizophrenia concept' (p.35). So, if schizophrenia cannot be proven to be a biological entity, then surely the validity of biological treatments as the main therapeutic option should also be questioned? In this scenario, the role of the psychiatrist would not be one of case or team manager, but purely as a consultant who would be asked to provide an opinion.

Secondly, the evidence base for recovery is extremely well researched. Box 4 provides a selection of just some of the papers and books available.

Box 4. Selected Resource List on Recovery.

- Anthony, W. (1993). Recovery from mental illness: The guiding vision of the mental health service system in the 1990s. Psychosocial Rehabilitation Journal, 16, 11–23.
- Anthony, W. (2000). A recovery-oriented service system: Setting some system level standards. Psychiatric Rehabilitation Journal, 24, 159–168.
- Baker, S., & Strong, S. (2001). Roads to recovery: How people with mental health problems recover and find ways of coping. London: Mind Publications.
- Butterworth, R., & Dean, J. (2000). Putting the missing rungs into the vocational ladder. Life in the Day, 4, 5–9.
- Davidson, L., & Strauss, J. (1992). Sense of self in recovery from severe mental illness. British Journal of Medical Psychology, 65, 131–145.
- Copeland, M. E. (1997). WRAP: Wellness Recovery Action Plan. Brattleboro, VT: Peach Press.
- Deegan, P. E. (1988). Recovery: The lived experience of rehabilitation. Psychosocial Rehabilitation Journal, 11, 11–19.
- Deegan, P. E. (1996). Recovery as a journey of the heart. Psychiatric Rehabilitation Journal, 19, 91–97.

• Department of Health (2001). The journey to recovery: The Government's vision for mental health care. London: Department of Health.

• Faulkner, A., & Layzell, S. (2000). Strategies for living: A summary report of user-led research into people's strategies for living with mental distress. London: Mental Health Foundation.

• Herman, J. L. (1992). Trauma and recovery. New York: Basic Books.

• Jamison, K. R. (1995). An unquiet mind: A memoir of moods and madness. New York: Alfred A. Knopf.

• Kleinman, A. (1988). The illness narratives: Suffering, healing and the human condition. New York: Basic Books.

• Liberman, R. P., & Kopelowicz, A. (2002). Recovery from schizophrenia: A challenge for the twenty-first century. International Review of Psychiatry, 14, 245–255.

• May, R. (2004). Understanding psychotic experience and working towards recovery. In P. McGorry & J. Gleeson (Eds.), Psychological interventions in early psychosis (pp. 245-260). Chichester: Wiley.

• McGorry, P. D. (1992). The concept of recovery and secondary prevention in psychotic disorders. Australian and New Zealand Journal of Psychiatry, 26, 3–17.

• Mental Health Foundation. (2002). Something inside so strong: Strategies for surviving mental distress. London: Mental Health Foundation.

• National Institute for Clinical Excellence (NICE). (2002). Schizophrenia: Core interventions in the treatment and management of schizophrenia in primary and secondary care. Clinical Guideline 1. London: NICE.

• Queensland Health. (2005). Sharing responsibility for recovery: Creating and sustaining recovery orientated systems of care for mental health. Available online at: www.health.qld.gov.au

• Ralph, R. O., Lambert, D., & Kidder, K. A.(2002). The recovery perspective and evidence-based practice for people with serious mental illness. A Guideline Developed for The Behavioural Health Recovery Management Project.

• Repper, J. (2000). Adjusting the focus of mental health nursing: Incorporating service users' experiences of recovery. Journal of Mental Health, 9, 575–587.

• Repper, J., & Perkins, R. (2003) Social inclusion and recovery. London: Baillière Tindall.

• Ridgeway, P. A. (2000). Re-storying psychiatric disability: Learning from first person narrative accounts of recovery. Psychiatric Rehabilitation Journal, 24, 335–343.

• Roberts, G. A. (2000). Narrative and severe mental illness: What place do stories have in an evidence-based world? Advances in Psychiatric Treatment, 6, 432–441.

• Romme, M., Escher, S., Dillon, J., Corstens, D., & Morris, M. (Eds.), (2009). Living with voices: Fifty stories of recovery. Ross-on-Wye, UK: PCCS Books.

• Royal College of Psychiatrists. (2004). Rehabilitation and recovery now (Council Report CR121). London: Royal College of Psychiatrists.

• Sheehan, A. (2002). Inspirations: A photographic record of recovery. London: NIMHE.

• Tait, L., Birchwood, M., & Trower, P. (2003). Predicting engagement with services for psychosis: Insight, symptoms and recovery style. British Journal of Psychiatry, 182, 123–128.

• Unzicker, R. (1989). On my own: A personal journey through madness and re-emergence. Psychosocial Rehabilitation Journal, 13, 70–77.

Finally, much has been written about the role of institutionalisation and learned helplessness as a product of the mental health systems. That they exist is not in doubt, although there are still some professionals who cling to the idea that withdrawal and lack of motivation is somehow linked to 'secondary' or 'negative symptoms' of illness. It is my contention that many of these behaviours are in fact a product of how the system treats people who are diagnosed with long-term enduring mental health problems. Most people in the UK diagnosed with schizophrenia are told that they have a chronic, degenerative condition and that they will be on medication for the rest of their lives. Some patients, for example, recount being told by psychiatrists that they would be better off with cancer on the grounds it would be 'easier to cure' (Longden, 2010). This in itself is debilitating, in that it implies that recovery is not an option.

There are numerous examples available of people who have got on with their lives after being informed that their condition is incurable. However, there are many more who, upon being told they have a lifelong illness, have subsequently become total victims of their condition (an effect often compounded by people being told not to have any great ambitions for their lives). Given this starting point, it is no wonder that many clients who have been in services for a number of years are incredulous and unresponsive to the concept of recovery. Even here we as a system bear the greatest responsibility, for it is a systemic approach to the idea of lifelong illness that leads to the client's belief that they cannot recover. The current dominance of a maintenance model therefore ensures recovery is blocked; and since maintenance is dominated by a medical view of mental distress, it is small wonder that clients do not feel motivated to recover.

Even today, with many clients being treated in the community, we have created a system dependency. Far from getting rid of institutionalisation, we have merely transferred the institution from building-based institutions to community-based institutions. We must recognise that institutionalisation is not about buildings (although they play a part). Rather, it is about attitudes, values, and practice.

Given the above, it is difficult not to conclude that the system itself is part of the problem rather than part of the solution. It therefore comes as no surprise that there is a growing body of opinion calling for mental health services to be removed from the NHS and brought into the voluntary sector. Although this scenario may appear extreme, it has nonetheless already become a viable one in England, the USA, New Zealand, and Canada. Frontline services, such as assertive outreach, continuing care, case management, and rehabilitation services, are being run by the independent and voluntary sectors, and it is not such a great shift to envisage the voluntary sector running ward-based services such as acute in-patient care. It is my opinion that this will happen if the statutory sector maintains its ostrich posture of burying its head in the sand and hoping that recovery, and the implications of recovery, will just go away.

Collaboration and Reconfiguration

In many respects it is clear that we can consider the statutory sector to be dysfunctional and, as a result of this dysfunction, unable to deliver recovery-based services. Indeed, far from needing to engage the statutory sector in recovery, there is a growing case for why it should not be involved in the delivery of mental health services. In this final section, I will explore a different way forward: a way that recognises the role of the statutory sector as partner organisations in an integrated service system that plays to organisational strengths.

It is evident that the NHS and Social Services by themselves cannot deliver the required recovery outcomes in mental health services. Therefore, we must look to creating a more optimally balanced system of service delivery, in which the statutory sector accepts that it can only work as an equal partner with other agencies in order to deliver recovery outcome-based and recovery-orientated services. This does not deny the need for a full range of treatment options to be available, but that treatments we use in the future must be effective in delivering recovery outcomes.

Recovery practice does not necessarily mean an absence of clinical interventions, such as medication, crisis support, or residential care, but it does mean that their use should be applied in such a way that they encourage rather than encumber the recovery process. Peter Chadwick (1997), a psychologist who has been diagnosed with schizophrenia, similarly states that:

> Recovering from psychosis is an individual journey that needs a wide variety of therapeutic options to be available to the person. Without the right options the attraction of psychosis or the close experience of substance 'misuse' may become the preferred option over the unbearable 'reality' of the person's present and past life. (p. 81)

The need, then, is to create a whole-life approach to mental well being that facilitates recovery in all areas of life (i.e. worthwhile employment, income, access to education, lasting and supportive social relationships, effective treatment, and decent housing) and not only through the input of mental health services, but also from the individual themselves, family, friends, generic community services, and consumer groups and organisations. Conversely, our current piecemeal system, far from creating an environment in which recovery can flourish, generally only succeeds in maintaining the status quo. This cannot be acceptable. We must look to developing a systemic approach that encompasses the whole system on an organisational level, and the whole life on an individual level (see Figure 1). For example, while progress has been made through the introduction of more effective clinical interventions (e.g. atypical neuroleptics and service models like functionalised community teams), we have not seen the significant improvement in the quality of life for service users that we could have hoped for. A good example of this is the fact that the recovery rate from psychosis in the UK has remained reasonably consistent at around 33% (combined social and clinical recovery measures: in other words, the 'best outcome'). In comparison, recovery rates are considerably higher in countries that, often as a result of circumstances, have a more whole-life approach to mental health care (e.g. 86% in Ibadan, Nigeria; and 87% Madhya Pradesh, India).

We should not, however, fall into the trap of re-inventing the wheel. Much work has been done on this, in particular by John Jenkins and colleagues, who have gone some way to developing a system of service delivery that seeks to deliver a joined-up approach to individuals in distress. In effect, they have taken the best parts of systems from around the world and moulded them into a whole-life approach to the individual. The National Plan, and the four priority areas for service development in Scotland, set out a clear framework to assist providers, purchasers, carers, and service users in having a greater clarity about that which needs to be developed in order for service users' real needs to be met. Over the last fifty years there has been an ongoing

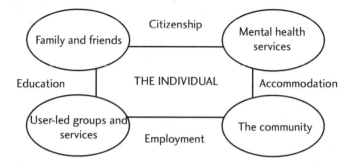

Figure 1. A whole-life approach to recovery (based on Trainor, Pomeroy, & Pape, 1993)

attempt to develop a whole-systems approach to replace the institutionalised styles of service provision that currently exist. The four priority areas have orientated services into thinking much more about a humanistic approach to both service development and delivery that will create the opportunity for real community integration to take place. Development of mental health services that embrace the full implication of the National Plan in its entirety will require people to adopt local solutions that go beyond simple reconfiguration of existing staff, services, or resources. This will require a broader perspective to be taken across the full spectrum of needs that service users have and the diversity of opportunities for collaboration with local community resources. As Jenkins has observed, achieving the vision of a 'whole life' approach will require all stakeholders to embrace some common principles of learning and collaboration as well as to explore, reconcile and operationalise shared values and principles that underpin social inclusion and recovery.

In recent times, even the most biologically-minded psychiatrists have shifted their positions somewhat on the causation of schizophrenia, moving from a purely biological construct of illness to one in which the role of the social environment is given greater emphasis. A good example of this is Professor Robin Murray (2002), who stated in an article on the latest advances in the management of psychoses:

> Biological researchers like me have, for the last twenty years, promoted a very medical model view of schizophrenia as a brain disease and have rather ignored the social environment. This has had an unfortunate consequence of deflecting attention from the social condition in which many people with schizophrenia live. Indeed, our society is ordered in a very strange way. We expect very vulnerable patients to live in situations that we could not tolerate. (p. 22)

Later in the same paper he goes on to say:

> We all accept that such social conditions can cause relapse in psychosis but until now we have not thought much about whether they contribute to the onset of the illness. (Ibid, p. 22)

If even the most biological psychiatrists are beginning to accept the role of society in terms of causation, then it stands to reason that the role of society in terms of recovery will be equally important. The question we must answer, therefore, is how do we best deliver services in the future to enable the recovery process? Though it might appear that services are constantly being reconfigured to meet the changing needs of society, the reality is that real change is minimal. It is my contention that change is not only required in the configuration of mental health services themselves, but in who delivers what services. I believe there is a case for the statutory sector to retract back to core business concepts. This would mean its main functions become crisis assessment and resolution, older people's services, and some specialist services such as early intervention and perhaps assertive outreach. Crisis resolution would not only be dealing with the acute phase of a person's distress, but also kick-starting recovery through a sound planning process that is person-centred and outcome-focused. Initial assessment and screening would be a primary care function, most of which would be carried out within the GP's surgery by psychiatric nurses employed by the practice. Routine treatments such as depots, anxiety management, anger management, and brief solution-focused therapy would also become a primary care responsibility. In this scenario, the voluntary sector would have the responsibility for implementing people's recovery plans via a case manager who would contract with providers to deliver services as agreed in the recovery plan. Individual contracts would replace the current block contracts, therefore ensuring that the value base of recovery (rather than the value of a block contract) would inform service development and delivery. Services such as crisis houses and residential recovery units would still operate on a block contract, but would have to clearly demonstrate person-centred approaches for the clients using such services. This would apply to all residential and/or housing support contracts, ensuring that recovery was the central tenet for service delivery.

Many voluntary organisations in Scotland have already progressed someway down the road of preparing their systems, policies, and practice to meet the challenges of the recovery agenda. There is a need for this to be replicated within the statutory sector, and it may be the case that to achieve this in mental health would mean that the services provided within this sector would have to be separated from the rest of the NHS to ensure that the resources earmarked for mental health stay in mental health. If we are to achieve genuine recovery, then the need to move towards a social care solution rather than a medically derived solution is, in my opinion, where we need to start. Change is always hard and painful, but the failure to change will only lead to the unnecessary waste of peoples' lives in systems that are already failing them. The Scottish Executive has started the process of recovery in policy terms: it is up to us to deliver in real terms.

Chapter Seven

RECOVERING RECOVERY: THE ROLE OF PERSON-CENTRED PLANNING

Good recovery planning can ensure a person's journey through the mental health system has an end as well as a beginning. It is important that a person's sense of self is maintained throughout the whole procedure. Figures 1-3 help to conceptualise the processes that can destroy or promote the personal identity of those people who experience mental distress:

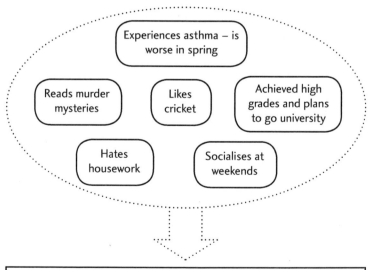

Figure 1. Prior to onset of illness and diagnosis.

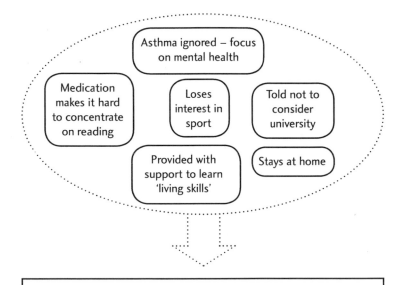

Figure 2. Increasing identification with mental distress and psychiatric diagnosis.

Many people become trapped at the level of increased identification with illness (Figure 3) because of the reinforced messages that work to create distress and illness as a dominant identity and reality. The role formal service provision plays in this process, either overtly or covertly, cannot be overstated. The safety of identification with illness may even be too great for someone to extend their comfort zone and gain their citizenship again. This is most likely to result when systems communicate low expectations for people to contribute to their own wellbeing. According to the psychiatrist Mark

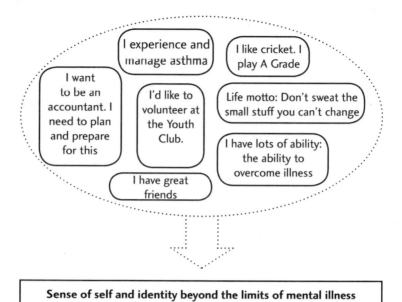

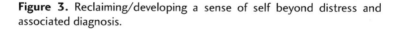

Sense of self and identity beyond the limits of mental illness

Figure 3. Reclaiming/developing a sense of self beyond distress and associated diagnosis.

Ragins (2006), a key difference between a person-centred and an illness-centred approach is that while the former places relationships at its foundation and commences with welcoming and engagement, the latter places diagnosis at its core and begins with an illness assessment. Furthermore, he notes that while person-centred provision works towards quality of life goals and is largely goal driven, illness-centred services focus on diagnosis, illness reduction, and the concept of symptoms and disability.

If change is to really happen, then there is a need for services to shift from a maintenance model towards a recovery process. The recovery process is made up of a number of key elements. These are:

- Holistic model
- Responsibility
- Informed risk-taking
- Alternative therapies
- Core beliefs of team members
- High staff expectations
- Rights and advocacy
- Social inclusion
- Social networks
- Empowerment/choice – person taking control of own life
- Self-determination
- Interdependence
- Coping strategies
- Potential to exit services

If there is a model involved in the recovery process, then it is important that this model is holistic. It is clear that the medical model can sit comfortably within a holistic framework, whereas a *holistic model* does not sit easily within the medical model. The recovery process encourages the client to take *responsibility*, and as a consequence staff are encouraged to view informed *risk-taking* in a positive way. The recovery process will always be open to *alternative therapies* and give them equal credence with traditional treatments. If recovery is a core belief within a team, then it stands to reason that staff within the team will have high expectations of both themselves and their clients. The recovery process will ensure that clients' rights are protected and that there is access to advocacy. Recovery practice is inclusive and encourages clients to expand their social networks in order to be included in society at large.

Within recovery-based services clients will have real choice and empowerment and be in control of the process. Recovery practice encourages self-determination for both clients and workers and recognises that no human can be independent: rather we are interdependent – that is, dependent on each other. It is important that we acknowledge that clients, like ourselves, have already developed their own coping strategies and as workers we should encourage clients to develop them further. The most important thing to remember as workers committed to enabling recovery is to seek to make ourselves redundant in our clients lives: focusing on this will ensure that we are always seeking ways of allowing our clients to exit services: that recovery is not only possible, but is in fact inevitable.

Care Planning vs. Recovery Planning

In recovery-based services, care planning is often called recovery planning and the plan will be directed and owned by the person concerned, the main focus being on their own needs as identified by themselves. Each client must be allowed to choose those who will be involved in their planning process. If the recovery value base is to be translated into practice, then placing the individual at the centre of planning processes is fundamental.

Planning approaches should be fluid and flexible and be easily adapted to individual differences and changes. The recovery plan should not constrain the recovery process rather it must enable it. Failure to follow even these simple rules will often mean that the recovery process will fail.

If recovery is to become the flagship of modern mental health service provision then we must fully embrace both the values and the practice of recovery. This is especially true when planning interventions that will be used with people. Table 1 depicts the main differences between the standard care planning approach (CPA) and recovery planning. The main point to note is that recovery planning builds on standard care planning; it is not a new way of planning, rather it is the natural evolution of CPA.

CPA CARE PLANS	RECOVERY PLANS
Identify the interventions and anticipated outcomes	Interventions address all areas of relevance to the person, as identified in the assessment process
	Contributions from significant others and community based agencies are recognised and alternative options included, especially peer-run and peer support services
	Desired outcomes are defined by the individual themselves
	Plans and outcomes are future focused
Record all actions necessary to achieve the agreed goals	Strategies to promote and maintain wellness are identified
	Actions to be taken are broken down so that each step is timely and achievable
In the event of disagreement include the reasons	All views about goals are clearly stated
	A plan for achieving all identified goals is articulated in detail
Give an estimated time scale by which the goals will be achieved or reviewed	Timescale is decided by the person concerned and includes dates for formally reviewing the helpfulness of treatment/service provision and other support with the option of the person amending the timescales

CPA CARE PLANS	RECOVERY PLANS
Detail the contribution of all agencies involved	Includes a list of all supporters (informal and formal) who have a role to play within the plan
	Chosen advocates are clearly identified
	The person takes responsibility for their own part in making the plan work
	Clarifies communication between all those named, making explicit what will be recorded and with whom the service user has agreed details can be shared
Include appropriate crisis contingency planning	Records coping strategies used in the past
	Identifies triggers and early warning signs and responses to them. Includes a detailed crisis plan that accounts for the situations most likely to occur
	Details the agreed decision-making process to be adopted (including in crisis situations)

Person-Centred Planning

In his analysis of the Hearing Voices Network (HVN), McLaughlin (in Parker et al., 1995, p. 123) states that the movement 'Challenges the "reality" of mental illness, and redefines areas of experience outside the psychiatric apparatus.' This redefinition of experience also happens to professionals when they start to think about recovery and wellness instead of illness. Thinking in these terms shifts the professional focus towards person-centred approaches, which go far beyond our current CPA and case management approaches to care. Instead, professionals find for themselves a redefinition 'of experience outside the psychiatric apparatus'. This is perhaps most apparent, at least for some individuals, in the way nurses change their practice when they start to work in the community instead of the hospital. By basing themselves in the community, nurses directly confront the reality of their clients' lives. They witness the poverty, stigma, and loneliness that their clients endure on a daily basis and, in many instances, find themselves acting as advocates in terms of benefit agencies, housing departments, and such like. This changing role can cause many to question not only the values of society, but also the treatment regimes that they were responsible for.

Whilst this move to the community (and its consequent role change) can be important for developing the recovery role of nursing, the most significant development is the extent to which nurses may start questioning their clients' treatment regimes. I believe that this is the first factor for any professional wanting to change how they work. The need to question is also an essential tool that professionals must use when working with clients. Not only should they question society and their clinical interventions, they should also question such factors as their clients' beliefs and behaviours. Indeed I would go further, and suggest that the role of the professional is to question everything. Questions are at the core of the recovery process for professionals, and because of this it is important that the right questions are asked when working with clients. One of the main weaknesses professionals have is their reliance on previous clinical notes when receiving a referral. In my opinion, the mistake that many make at this point is to work from the referral letter, or the accompanying notes, rather than start with a blank sheet. If the professional is going to work within a recovery framework, it is essential that they start from scratch: and that means assessing the client as if it was their first time in the system. The blind acceptance of referral data is tantamount to saying that nothing has, or can, change for the client.

From 1998-2001 I worked in the North Birmingham Assertive Outreach Team (UK), where I witnessed first-hand the importance of moving towards a recovery model of working, and in applying personal recovery plans with all clients who wish to use them. This type of plan was not some convoluted advance in the planning of care. Rather, it was a common-sense approach to people and their problems. From the very beginning it placed the client at the centre of the process, and this emphasis runs throughout, with clients having the freedom to choose whether to use the plan or not, when and how to complete it, who should help them write it, where the finished plan or copies of the plan will be kept, and who can have access to it.

The plan's definition of recovery rejects the traditional focus on 'symptom' cessation, instead stressing the significance of coping, control, developing skills, achieving one's goals, and fulfilling one's dreams. The client's responsibility to commit to (and be prepared to work towards) achieving these outcomes is similarly emphasised. Clients are advised to leave out any parts of the plan if they feel it does not apply to them, and are encouraged to reflect on the fact that if they cannot be honest with themselves, or take responsibility for their own recovery, then they are probably not ready to use the plan. This is the type of honest planning that is needed by all sides if a recovery model is to work. Similarly, professionals are encouraged to replace their traditional emphasis on difficulties, diagnosis, and symptoms, with an exploration of client strengths, priorities, and positives (which can be developed as tools for problem solving difficulties).

The most important point is that both the professionals in the team and the clients that used the service developed the plan collaboratively. This means that the honesty I alluded to earlier is situated on both sides. Such frankness can break down the barriers that exist between professionals and clients, and with it bring new terms of engagement that can turn assertive outreach from being perceived as aggressive into active outreach based on positive engagement. Using this type of recovery plan goes a long way to making positive engagement a reality.

The content of the plan is simple to understand and is divided into seven stages: (1) what recovery means to me; (2) about myself; (3) difficulties; (4) coping; (5) the mental health system and treatments; (6) plans for change, and (7) your personal development plan (PDP). It is worth noting at this point that it is not until stage seven (the final stage) that the client starts their PDP. The reason for this is that the first six stages are essentially information gathering, and it is by looking back through the other six stages that enables the client to create an effective development plan. A workable plan requires a joint approach – an alliance – between the professional and client involved. This planning tool without doubt does exactly that, in that it cannot work without the active participation of both sides. The role of the professional within the recovery process becomes ever clearer: it is that of an enabler. It is their capacity as an enabler that allows professionals to reach their full potential as agents of recovery. The checklist in Box 5 provides some suggestions of issues that workers and clients can develop and explore together within a recovery planning process.

Box 5. Recovery Planning Checklist.

✓ All plans to be developed collaboratively over time

✓ Planning is more effective in the context of a good therapeutic relationship

✓ Views of the individual and their significant others should be incorporated into the planning process

✓ Develop plans that are future-focused

✓ Language should be inclusive and accessible

✓ Successful coping strategies should be recorded

✓ Identify the person's strengths and abilities

✓ Areas such as personal, physical, spiritual, academic, sexual, and emotional needs should be considered, at the discretion of the individual

✓ Provide information about alternative support options, especially user-led and user-run programmes

✓ Develop timelines that incorporate reviewing the helpfulness of treatment, and decisions about changes in the plan

✓ Clearly indicate who is involved in the treatment/care process and the necessary communication strategy

✓ Provide a written copy of how to give feedback about the service (either general feedback and advice, making a complaint, or providing a compliment about service provision)

✓ Explain and document the confidentiality process – who does the service provider need to discuss individual details with, and who does the service user want details withheld from?

✓Identify triggers and early warning signs (and helpful responses to these) and incorporate them into a Prevention Plan

✓Develop a detailed crisis plan that accounts for the most likely situations which could occur

✓Identify activities that support and maintain wellbeing

✓List both formal and informal supporters who have a role to play within the plan. Chosen advocates should be clearly identified

✓Record who is responsible for the completion of different tasks and the time required to accomplish these (e.g. care coordinator to provide information on medication within one week; service user to find out cost of gym membership within two weeks). Break down tasks and goals so that each step appears timely and achievable

The COPS Recovery Programme

There is little point in criticising our present system if there are no improvements to offer. In this section, I intend to argue that there is a viable alternative way in which people with mental health problems can recover. Like any other journey, the recovery journey has an itinerary. The itinerary I will be using is called the COPS recovery programme. COPS stands for Choice, Ownership, People, and Self, and is based on the elements I believe were responsible for my own recovery. COPS is not a programme of clinical or social recovery, though there may be outcomes that equate with these models. Rather, it is a programme for personal recovery.

Recovery is essentially a subjective thing, and as such is experienced differently by each individual. There are, however, some stepping stones that are consistent amongst those who successfully recover, and it is these stepping stones that comprise the COPS programme. In previous chapters, I discussed the role of self, ownership, and people. I will now provide an account of choice.

Choice

Most people in our society regard choice as a fundamental entitlement, and rightly so. Indeed, one can argue that a society's sophistication can be measured by the level of choice available to the individuals within it. In democracies, politicians go to great lengths to foster the notion of choice as the bedrock of society. For example, the Commission on Social Justice in the UK provided the following as one of four propositions in their report Social Justice Strategies for National Renewal (1994): 'We must promote real choices across the life-cycle, in the balance of employment, family, education, leisure and retirement.' (p. 21) According to the Commission, promoting these choices for every citizen is essential if a society is to be regarded as just. I would agree with this argument, and would further suggest that for a society to deny citizens these choices would make that society unjust. When the state uses its power to deny a psychiatric patient's choice, then the state is acting unjustly by denying them a chance of recovery.

The concept of choice is something that is frequently misconstrued by service providers as meaning that they make the decisions. Even where there is an element of choice, it is often only cosmetic in that the choices offered are rarely truly meaningful. Two good examples of this are in the areas of treatment and accommodation. All too often, the notion of choice is lost in these areas with clients being offered only the choice between one drug or another in terms of treatment, despite the fact that the Patient's Charter clearly states that all treatment alternatives should be discussed with the client. Both the client and the worker share joint responsibility for resolving this problem. There is little doubt that many doctors have no idea what alternatives are available to them beyond medication, and they and their professional bodies must take responsibility for rectifying this situation. In turn, clients and their advocates must take responsibility for challenging the medics by pointing out the rights that clients have under the Charter, and asking why alternative treatments have not been considered. Similarly, choice of accommodation is another area in which we are slow to learn any of the lessons from past mistakes. In the inner cities, it is still normal practice to move vulnerable clients out of acute wards and back into poor housing and/or run-down estates, which only increase their vulnerability and expedites a return to hospital. In many mental health services there is little or no choice offered in accommodation that could develop the recovery potential of the client. Indeed, one could argue that when we discharge clients back into a toxic environment, then we do little more than set them up for relapse.

Real choice is not only having the ability to pick from a number of predetermined options, it is about having the power to add options which you as a consumer would most like. Professional perceptions of the things clients need are one of the greatest barriers to choice, since much of their perception is biased by their professionalism. In order to achieve real choice, it is essential that we start without any assumptions as to the real desires of the client. However, even more important than professional perception is the voice of the client. If choice is to become a reality, then service users must begin to exercise their voices; they must make clear to professionals exactly what they want. One of my own memories of seeing the consultant in the ward round was how I always entered with lots of questions and came out with no answers. The main reason I never got any answers was that I always forgot the questions in the heat of the meeting. This was resolved when I finally agreed with my advocate to write down my questions before I went into the ward round. Though most of my questions still went unanswered, I at least had the satisfaction of knowing I had asked them.

Personal Development Plan (PDP)

Much of the supposed choice within services revolves around the workings of CPA or case management approaches (CMA). These tools would, if used properly, not only identify what professionals think the client needs but also what the client's aspirations are. All too often, however, CPA becomes nothing more than a medication review controlled by the medic. For this reason I believe that there is a need to be more direct in planning the recovery journey. Making good plans will enable a client to plot their own journeys and ensure that they stay on course throughout it. There are many ways of planning that are person-centred, although the one I most prefer is a PDP, much like the ones many professionals use in their own workplaces. The reason for this preference is that the focus of a PDP is very much on development rather than on care. This does not mean that we reject the concept of care; in my opinion, working in this way can only enhance the care quality by adding the notion of 'caring about' to the existing 'caring for' framework. Like most planning, a PDP requires the person to answer a series of questions, and Box 6 provides a selection that may be beneficial. They are fairly open-ended in that they can relate to health, social activities, employment, or training, as well as allowing the client to examine strengths, weaknesses, opportunities, and threats in their personal life. Many of the questions appear straightforward, but when was the last time we were asked them by others, or indeed asked them of ourselves? Indeed, if used properly by all parties, this analysis can guide the recovery process by allowing the client to monitor their own progress against the goals they have set themselves. Furthermore, they can help shift service provision from the passive doing for framework to the more empowering concept of doing with (Carling et al., 1999).

Box 6. Questions to Consider for a Personal Development Plan

1. What areas of your life do you consider have gone particularly well over the last six months?

2. What can be done by yourself, or others, to build on your successes?

3. What areas of your life have not gone so well in the last six months?

4. Have there been any particular barriers, difficulties, or problems that have caused these parts of your life not to go so well?

5. What can you do by yourself to resolve these problems?

6. What can others do to help you resolve these problems?

7. What do you want to achieve over the next six months?

8. Which of these goals can you achieve on your own?

9. Which of these goals do you require help to achieve?

10. Who can help you achieve these goals?

One of the most important aspects of choice is in the selection of people that support the client. The usual practice of appointing a key-worker without consulting the client is not only wrong but can, in some circumstances, be dangerous both to the client and the professional. This danger has nothing to do with the threat of violence posed by the client, but the lack of progress that will occur if there is no positive relationship between the client and the professional. How often do we ask client and key-worker whether they are happy working together? Even if we did ask, and found that they were unhappy, would we act on the answer? I would hope so, though I fear the system would not always respond in a helpful and appropriate way.

In services that do allow clients to choose their own workers, both clients and staff agree that the system eliminates many of the relationship problems created by the traditional system. Other benefits are that a trusting relationship can be established much more quickly, thereby accelerating the recovery process. Even if an organisation cannot adopt a policy of allowing clients to choose their paid supporters, it must at least find a way of allowing clients to change their worker if they wish to do so. If this simple step could be achieved, then it is my opinion that the benefit in terms of recovery would far outweigh any loss of face that may occur amongst professionals.

The PIE Approach

Even when we work in a person-centred way, there is a danger that we will end up turning person-centred working into a model, not least because we are often conditioned by our professional training to think in terms of models. Yet the minute we do this we will have failed, for the very act of creating a model denies the individualistic approach. To counter this, I will now introduce you to my preferred style for working with individuals. In my opinion PIE is an advanced approach to care that, if used properly, makes no assumptions either overtly or covertly. PIE stands for 'play it by ear', and it is the only way that you can truly take a person-centred approach and apply it to numerous people. Using PIE allows you to easily create a service around a person rather than fitting a person into existing services. In essence it is reactive, in that you are developing a service in response to present circumstances. Since most services (even in acute care) are based on this principal of reactive response, then this concept should prove no problem for professionals to implement.

A Case Example: Jenny

I first used PIE in the mid 1990s when I was approached by a woman (I will call her Jenny; she has given me permission to write her story) who asked me if I would work with her to resolve her voices. At that time I did not work with individuals, so I told her no. Jenny was one of those people who did not take no for an answer, and she took to asking me at regular intervals if I would reconsider. Eventually she wore me down and I agreed to meet with her. I confess that my agenda was to make this first meeting our last, but after hearing her story I was hooked, and we agreed to meet again to start working through her voices. The following is a précis of the work we did together and the results of our work (or should I say her work).

The first thing Jenny did was to tell her life story, which in a very shortened version went like this: Jenny's parents divorced when she a child; she lived with her mother and had no contact with her father. Her mother met a new partner, who Jenny liked initially, and when she proceeded to marry him Jenny got herself a stepfather. Although everything was good at the beginning, it was not long before the new stepfather began to take an interest in Jenny: not as a daughter, but as an object that he could abuse. This continued for about two years before Jenny finally told her grandmother what was happening to her. The grandmother told Jenny's mother, who refused to believe it, and in frustration the grandmother finally took Jenny to live with her. Her grandmother did not go to the authorities for fear that she too would lose Jenny, and Jenny was also very clear that she did not fault her grandmother for this. Indeed, Jenny felt her grandmother had done a good job in bringing her up. Jenny married when she was in her late teens and divorced in her mid-twenties. She had two children during the marriage. Her grandmother died when she was twenty-two, which left her feeling very alone since she did not talk to her mother, who was still married to Jenny's abuser.

Jenny started hearing an occasional voice when she was in her late teens, but thought nothing of it. During the break-up of her marriage her voices became much worse, and it was at this time that she came to the attention of psychiatric services. She was ultimately given a diagnosis of paranoid schizophrenia and put on various neuroleptics, none of which relieved the voices. She was prone to self-harming and spent a lot of her hospital admissions being detained on Sections. She had finally managed to bring her self-injury under control, though she had not stopped completely. She had got this far through membership of a self-help group.

Jenny identified four voices. The first was male, very negative, always abusive and commanding. This voice would tell her that it was her fault, that she deserved everything that happened to her, and that she was a slut. This voice she knew was the voice of her stepfather. The second voice was a contrast to the first voice in every way: it was female, very positive, never hostile, and everything it said was soothing and helpful. This voice would tell Jenny that things would be okay that she (the voice) would protect her. Jenny knew this to be the voice of her grandmother. The third voice was the voice of a female child who would do nothing but scream all the time. In some ways this was the most difficult voice for Jenny, in that it never made any sense. It was only after some time that Jenny identified it as the voice of herself when she was being abused. The final voice was a male voice that was a mixture of everything. It was both positive and negative, abusive and nonabusive, advisory and commanding. We called it her neutral voice, and she knew it to be the voice of her ex-husband. Once we had a life history and a voice profile, Jenny was able to relate the voices to her life experience and decide that her real problem was not actually the voices, but the fact that she had been sexually abused and that this issue had never been properly resolved.

Before we could go any further with the voices work, Jenny had to carry out one of the most difficult and lonely tasks that anyone who has been abused has to do. That is, she had to find herself innocent of any fault within the abuse. This is something that everyone who has been abused has to come to terms with at some point if recovery is going to become a reality. The voice of the abuser told Jenny that it was her fault that the abuse happened, and like many people who hear the voice of their abuser(s), Jenny was inclined to believe that she did play some part in 'leading him on'. It did not matter that I, like many others, told Jenny that she was the victim in this situation. What mattered is what Jenny thought were the facts. Jenny had to put herself on trial, and in order to do this she had to go through the experience again and again from every conceivable angle until she could say with real conviction 'I am innocent'. This is no easy task, and anyone who has done it will tell you that not only is it painful, it is also exhausting and often it initially makes the voices worse. Once this was done Jenny and I discussed how best to work with the voices. Her desire was to get rid of them, though she knew that at best she would probably only succeed in developing coping strategies that would allow her to get on with her life.

We decided that the best way forward was to enter into a dialogue with her voices and that we would do this with one voice at a time, starting with the most positive voice first. In other words we would do what most professionals believe we should never do: actively engage with the voices. The first attempt was almost a complete disaster, and with hindsight it was my fault as I underestimated the resistance that I would encounter from the voice of the grandmother. I started by asking Jenny if she could ask her grandmother if she would talk to me. Jenny's reply astonished me at the time: the voice of the grandmother wanted to know why she should talk to me, and why I wanted to help Jenny. It took three meetings before the grandmother would stop questioning my motives and start talking about how we might help Jenny (after the process was over, we concluded that the questions of the voice actually related to Jenny's own fears about the journey we were starting). After the initial breakthrough, the grandmother agreed to help Jenny and I deal with the voice of the stepfather. We then decided that the next voice to approach was that of her ex-husband.

This was a complete waste of time: the voice played games with us for weeks on end before we finally decided that there would be no help for Jenny from this voice. (We came to the conclusion from this experience that some voices have very little or no significance when you are working through the voice hearing experience. Indeed that some voices are nothing more than red herrings.)

We then turned our attention to the child voice, and to our horror found that not only would the child not engage in any way with me, it would not engage with Jenny either. We spent many hours trying to forge a relationship with the child to no avail. Eventually we turned to the grandmother for help and asked her to negotiate with Jenny the child. The grandmother agreed, and she slowly managed to get Jenny the child to talk to us, although initially this was only through her (the grandmother). Over time, Jenny the child stopped screaming and did start to talk to us. She agreed that she had to confront the abuser, and we spent many hours preparing Jenny the child for this confrontation. (We had in effect forgotten one of the rules of working with voices, which is to play to your strengths. We had started the process by enlisting the aid of the grandmother, and then once getting it we had essentially left her out of the process. In actual fact, she was to prove the key to Jenny the child as a voice, just as she had been the ally of Jenny when the abuse occurred in real life. It also made me acutely aware of the importance of the interactions between different voices that people hear.)

When the voice of Jenny the child told us she was ready to confront the abuser, we decided to make two days available for the confrontation. Jenny arrived one Friday afternoon and we chatted for a couple of hours, not about voices or how she was feeling, but just relaxing. Then on Saturday morning we got down to work. The Jenny the child voice told the abuser exactly what she felt: that it was he who should have left the family home, that it was he who was the perpetrator, and that she was the victim. She told him that she was innocent and that he was guilty, that she had the right to hate him, and no longer felt that she was evil. She repeated much of this over the course of the day. Every time the abuser voice tried to regain control of the situation, Jenny the child would be backed up by Jenny, the grandmother, and myself. By the end of that day, although we were exhausted, we both knew something had changed and that much had now been resolved. Even now though, it was not as we had expected it to be. There were no great victory celebrations, only the quiet that follows any major battle. It was some weeks later before we sat down together to look at what had happened since the day of the confrontation.

There had been some remarkable changes in the voices that Jenny was hearing. The abuser voice was no longer dominant, although it was still there. We surmised from this that the reason it had not gone completely was that while Jenny had dealt with the abuse, she could not become un-abused. That is, she could not change what had happened, only her response. The grandmother voice had now become dominant, which was okay for Jenny as its presence was always positive. It was the disappearance of the child voice that was the most significant change, and we concluded that this was the result of Jenny no longer needing to dissociate from her past. Indeed, we believed that Jenny the adult and Jenny the child voice became Jenny the person. These changes have now remained constant in her life ever since. Without doubt Jenny has reclaimed her life: she has recovered.

My role in this process was minimal. I played only a

bit part, and it was Jenny who did all the hard work. I only created the space in which she could do it. It is clear to me that this is one of the main roles that professionals can play when working with clients. Individuals who are working through complex recovery journeys require this type of support to enable them to complete their journeys successfully, and I cannot believe that this is an impossible shift for professionals to make. Indeed, I would argue that many already do these types of interventions, and that many more wish to do so. My advice for these professionals is simple: do it.

Chapter Eight

WAR OR PEACE, WHAT'S IT TO BE?

I have submitted to a new control. A power is gone, which nothing can restore: A deep distress hath humanised my soul.
William Wordsworth

One dictionary definition of distress is: mental pain or anguish. It is also described as: another word for depressed.

In this short passage from Wordsworth, this mental pain, this anguish, this depression, is a humanising factor. Not for Wordsworth the notion that distress is dehumanising, as it is portrayed today. Not for Wordsworth the reduction of distress into a biological framework or the devaluation of experience. Rather, Wordsworth seeks to find meaning in distress as a way to come closer to the person beneath the experience. The realities of the emotions are something that cannot be denied. Instead, they are to be acknowledged as a part of the recovery.

In psychiatry the emphasis on pathology and biology brings with it a reliance on pharmacology to provide the answers. Psychiatry has taken to the field of battle armed only with a prescription pad – and nothing else of any real relevance. Psychiatrists are running into battle against distress carrying their ICD-10s and their British National Formulas, and faring just about as well as the Polish cavalry did against Hitler's Panzer tanks: clearly losing the war, but fighting on valiantly because occasionally one of their drug cocktails has some small beneficial effect on a particular person.

They are casualties, all of them: casualties of a profession that has stopped breathing but refuses to recognise its own demise. The smell of fear is thick around them as they face their enemy, knowing that sometimes they can do little, but more often they can do nothing. They are an army of white coats and stethoscopes slipping and sliding in a quagmire of people's misfortune.

The leadership of the Royal College of Psychiatry continues to act like aging generals of the First World War, still sending their troops over the top in the hope of gaining glory by curing a few, only to see them defeated time and time again by illness that is not illness. They are blind these generals, blind to the human response to experience, blind to human variation, blind to the fact that they do not have all the answers.

They are arrogant, these generals. They are the high priests to the new god Pseudo-Science. Only they can define that which causes madness; only they have the knowledge to treat madness; only they can decide when an individual's madness has ended.

These generals are cowards, who wait at the rear of the battle and refuse to engage directly with the enemy. As they wait, these wordsmiths of the war engage in games of theory without any hint of practice, protecting themselves with the knowledge that if it all goes wrong they can always blame the other side.

And they are fools, these generals: they fool themselves by only looking at their successes, and they fool their patients' families into thinking that they, the doctors, have the solution. They even try to fool the patients, and when that does not work and the patients question the generals, the generals become even more foolish by turning the patients into the enemy.

This, then, is the backdrop of the war – yes, war – that is being waged between psychiatry and so-called illness. It is a war that psychiatry finds itself fighting on three fronts. The first front is the scientific front, the second is with the clients of its own system, and the third is against a fifth column within its own ranks.

On the scientific front, the psychiatric theory of mental illness as a biological or genetic construct is beginning to look more and more like mysticism and less and less like good scientific theory. Areas of research such as the link between dopamine and schizophrenia, historically the unshakeable articles of faith in psychiatry, have been going badly wrong. Rather than research shoring up the foundations of the dopamine theory, it is finding massive holes that are shaking those foundations. Similarly, the concept of genetic causation for mental illness is being seriously challenged and contested.

On the client front there is a growing movement that psychiatrists have to face in open combat. Many of these clients started as I did by trusting their psychiatrist; they happily heard the doctors tell them that after ten days or so on medication they would start to feel better. Many waited the ten days, then ten weeks, then ten months. Some of them waited over ten years, and still nothing happened. So finally the patient became impatient and started to question the doctor. The doctor, shocked that the patient dared query their knowledge, tells the patient that questioning itself is part of the illness and is called lack of insight. So lacking in insight is the patient that they decide to no longer to comply with the doctor's wishes. Thinking to take control once more of their own life, they decide to go their own way.

Doctor's response: declare war. This ill person, who is so

lacking in insight, is now so ill that they will not do what they are told by the experts, and therefore need to be treated, like it or not. This person is now a noncompliant, an enemy of psychiatry, created by a false promise that would only last ten days before it would be broken.

It is at this stage that the patient may be drawn into the ranks of the user movement. They may move between different user organisations and then find a home in one or more of them. From there they are trained in the art of psychiatric warfare. It is here that they find comrades who have been through the same basic training on the wards of some mental hospital. It is here that they find access to information about the chemical warfare that has been waged on them; it is here that they discover that many of their so-called symptoms are nothing more than effects of these chemicals. It is here that their anger finally turns to action. For many it is here that they finally find themselves.

On now to the third front: a fifth column of doctors who have themselves become disillusioned with the war. These are mainly junior officers in the white-coated army, the ones who see the casualties of the war. For them, the casualties are not numbers or statistics, they are real, breathing, thinking people. For these officers, the end does not justify the means. For these officers a peace is needed: not a peace based on them having more control over people's lives, but a peace based on mutual respect, mutual dignity, power sharing, and choice. The generals, though, are deaf to the pleas of their own officers, just as they are deaf to the arguments of other professionals, just as they are deaf to the questions of their own clients.

Back now to our generals. What are they, when all is said and done, but arrogant, foolish, blind, deaf, cowards, who have forgotten the rebellion of their own youth, who have fallen for the seductive charms of power, who have forgotten the now disregarded oath of allegiance, the Hippocratic Oath, the very first tenet of which is do no harm?

Some may consider the war analogy as too strong for health, so let us look at another short passage from 'Strange Meeting', written by the great war poet Wilfred Owen: 'One sprang up and stared, with piteous recognition in fixed eyes, lifting distressful hands as if to bless.' I have seen that stare. I have seen that dim recognition in peoples' eyes. I have seen those shaking, distressed hands, moving involuntarily like a priest's blessing. But I did not see them in the killing fields of Aden or the Falklands, and I did not see them in the desert during the Gulf War. Where then did I see them then, these poor pathetic wounded creatures? I saw them in my local psychiatric unit, I saw them living rough in the streets of our major cities, I saw them living in hard-to-let houses in our inner-city housing estates, I saw them in the homeless hostels, I saw them yesterday, I see them now as I speak. Their lifeless eyes looking at me asking questions without speaking, yet saying so much.

Where then is the shame of the generals, where is the shame of the professionals, where is the shame of society, where is our shame, where is my shame?

'Do no harm': the first tenet of the Hippocratic Oath, broken time and time again in the quest for scientific justification. 'Do no harm', broken time and time again to continue the battlefield strategy of biological reductionism, a strategy that has failed for fifty years and will fail for the next fifty years. Do no harm, 15% of chronic schizophrenics will kill themselves, many because they cannot see an end to the horrors of their war. Do no harm, fifty-two people died last year because of the introduction of neuroleptics into their bodies. Do no harm, the most common reason for women presenting at Accident and Emergency departments is because of self-injury, yet nothing is done. Do no harm, in Romania there is no blood monitoring of those on Clozaril; if the patient dies, then the generals conclude that the drug was not right for that person. Do no harm, would these generals be found innocent by a jury of twelve citizens today of doing no harm?

This I cannot answer, and I do not expect you to either. I only expect you to think about it.

In 1997 the generals at the Bethlam and Maudsley hospital decided to celebrate 750 years of scientific advancement in psychiatry. They celebrated 750 years of being a hospital that cared for those who were deemed to be mad. They celebrated the last 750 years as if it had been a never-ending success story. They did not celebrate 750 years of paupers' graves, they did not celebrate the women locked up for daring to get pregnant when unmarried, they did not celebrate the men locked up for daring to be gay, they did not celebrate charging the wealthy an admission fee on Sundays to watch the lunatics perform, they did not celebrate the corruption of many of the superintendents. No, what they celebrated was something completely different. They celebrated a fantasy history of compassion and caring, a fantasy history of understanding and tolerance, a fantasy history of scientific breakthrough and achievement. Never did they count the cost, only their successes did they see with their tunnel vision. I have a different way of perceiving these 750 years that they dared to celebrate: I see them as years of pain and despair for the inmates. I see three ages of the psychiatric institution.

The first age: the age of religious barbarism, which saw

people shackled and chained to beds, beaten and tortured to drive out demons that only existed in the doctrines and minds of the priest/doctor.

The second age: the age of moral barbarism that used laws like the Vagrancy Act to incarcerate the poor, and reached its pinnacle in the warped morals of the Victorian era.

The third age: the age of scientific barbarism, which uses the surgeon's knife to cut out portions of people's brains, which uses electrodes to shock people, which uses drugs not only to treat people but, when treatment fails, to subdue and control them by turning them into zombies. An age that has combined chemical and psychological warfare with physical torture. An age that bastardises events and statistics with a finesse not even the New Labour spin-doctors could have aspired to.

This is my view of the three ages. But can there be a fourth age? Can there be a peace, can there be a new age of enlightenment, can there be an end to this futile struggle, a struggle in which both sides are victims, a struggle where none can win victory? Or must it be that the cries of the distressed only get louder, that the oppression used at the behest of the state only gets greater, that the war only gets bloodier until every bone in my body cries no no no no. I am tired of this war. Yet there can be no unconditional surrender for me, only a negotiated peace can suffice. And think colleagues, if we can achieve this then we can all win the real war; we can defeat the thing we call mental illness and win the battle for recovery.

The Road to Recovery

I hope that by now the road to recovery, while difficult, is no longer seen as impossible. There are some hard times ahead for clients and professionals both in their individual circumstances and from wider societal perspectives, and in this final section I hope to deal with some of these issues.

Whilst reading through some of the drafts of this book, my partner Karen commented on the fact that though I was dealing with recovery I had not written in any great detail about the bane of her professional life: the pseudo-relapse. What is the pseudo-relapse, you might ask? Simply put, it is when the client attributes normal responses to life events as the return of their illness. This is one of the greatest hurdles that those experiencing mental distress must overcome. It is so easy every time something goes wrong in our lives, either through the mistakes we make or through life trauma, to either blame our 'illness', or to fall back into it. It seems to me that it is somehow much harder for us to accept that we are humans, with all the fragility that goes with being a human being. Everyone has bad days, for if there were no bad days how would we know what a good day is? If we never felt sadness how would we know what happiness is? If we were never bad how would we know what good is? If we never went through inner conflict how would we know inner peace? By the same token, if we have never been mentally broken how can we tell what mental wholeness is? In that sense, having gone through mental distress and achieved recovery we can understand life in a way that a great many people never will. The reality, then, is that one of our biggest hurdles is ourselves. If we do not believe in our own ability to achieve recovery, how can we expect anyone else to believe in us?

Like Jenny in the preceding chapter, we must do the bulk of the work. Yes, supports can be identified and put in place; yes, we can go to therapists or take medication; yes, we can attend self-help groups and be part of campaigns against abuses in psychiatry. But unless we are prepared to do the hard, gruelling personal work to achieve our personal recovery, then recovery will always remain a word instead of a fact. Whilst it is true that this cannot happen in isolation from the rest of society, in the present climate we will often have to make it happen despite our society. We must politically tackle areas of policy that seek to maintain us in the illness role. One of the main areas that must be dealt with is the benefit system. It is my contention that one of the main causes of relapse today in the UK is the arrival on the doormat of a letter from the Department of Social Security inviting the person for a review of their Disabled Living Allowance (DLA). DLA is the great double-edged sword of the British system. On one hand it has enabled many service users to achieve economic freedom, allowing them to have a far greater quality of life. On the other hand, it takes this benefit away from them as soon as they show signs of recovery. This is often followed by a relapse that costs the government even more than maintaining the person's level of income would have. Surely it makes sense to scrap this nonsense and allow people the level of income that keeps them out of the system and on the recovery road.

It is also time for professionals to get their act together. They should not be agents of the state, they should be the enablers of their local communities. It is their task, more than anyone else's, to tackle the issue of stigma in our society. Stigma is the great disease that is destroying any chance of recovery for many, in which forcing those with mental health problems to hide them only perpetuates the myths that surround mental health. Mental wellness can only be achieved in a mentally well society and the professional must be at the forefront of creating this wellness.

Politicians have a duty to all their constituents, and that includes those with mental health problems. It is time for them to stop taking the short-term view of mental health, responding only to the tabloid press and the provocative ranting of individuals such as Marjorie Wallace. If the government cannot come on board a recovery train as the train drivers, then they will surely be responsible for future generations of misery. In the UK the government have passed a law allowing those deemed to have a personality disorder to be held indefinitely before they commit any offence. In the UK, it is common for service users who do not comply with the treatment wishes of the psychiatrist to have their diagnoses changed to personality disorder. In the UK not only have computers become Year 2000 compliant, so have users of mental health services. If politicians could see the sense of recovery-based services, then perhaps – just perhaps – they could help create a mental health system that people could go to with confidence rather than fear.

Recovery is happening and it is here to stay. It is time for all of us to embrace not just the theory, or the concept, but the practice and reality of recovery.

Enjoy yours.

References

Andrew, E., Gray, N. S., & Snowden, R. J. (2008). The relationship between trauma and beliefs about hearing voices: A study of psychiatric and non-psychiatric voice hearers. Psychological Medicine, 38, 1409-1417.

Bak, M., Krabbendam, L., Janssen, I., de Graaf, R., Vollebergh, W., & van Os, J. (2005). Early trauma may increase the risk for psychotic experiences by impacting on emotional response and perception of control. Acta Psychiatrica Scandinavica, 112, 360-366.

Baker, P. (1989). Hearing voices. Manchester, UK: The Hearing Voices Network.

Beck-Sander, A. (1999). Relapse prevention: A model for psychosis? Behaviour Change, 16, 191-202.

Bentall, R. P. (2004). Madness explained: Psychosis and human nature. London: Penguin.

Bickerton, D., Worrall, A., & Chaplin, R. (2009). Trends in the administration of electroconvulsive therapy in England. The Psychiatrist, 33, 61-63.

Birchwood, M. J., Fowler, D., & Jackson, C. (2000). Early intervention in psychosis: A guide to concepts, evidence and interventions. Oxford: Wiley-Blackwell.

Birchwood, M., Iqbal, Z., Chadwick, P., & Trower P. (2000). Cognitive approach to depression and suicidal thinking in psychosis 2. Testing the validity of a social ranking model. The British Journal of Psychiatry, 177, 522-528.

Blom, J. D. (2003). Deconstructing schizophrenia: An analysis of the epistemic and nonepistemic values that govern the biomedical schizophrenia concept. Amsterdam: Boom.

Boyd, M., & Nihart, M. (1998). Psychiatric nursing: Contemporary practice. Philadelphia: Lippincott.

Breggin, P. (1979). Electroshock: Its brain disabling effects. New York: Springer.

Breggin, P. (1994). Toxic psychiatry (2nd Edition). New York: St. Martin's Press.

Breggin, P. (1997). Brain-disabling treatments in psychiatry. New York: Springer.

Breggin, P. (1998). Electroshock: Scientific, ethical, and political issues. International Journal of Risk and Safety in Medicine, 11, 5–40.

British Psychological Society. (BPS). (2000). Recent advances in understanding mental illness and psychotic experiences. A report by the BPS division of clinical psychology. London: British Psychological Society.

Burton, R. (1621/2001). Anatomy of melancholy. New York: New York Review Books.

Carling, P. J. (1995). Return to community: Building support systems for people with psychiatric disabilities. New York: Guildford Press.

Carling, P. J., Allott, P., Smith, M., & Coleman, R. (1999). Directional paper 3: Principles of recovery for a modern community mental health system. Birmingham, UK: National Health Service Executive.

Chadwick, P. (1997). Recovery from psychosis: Learning more from patients. Journal of Mental Health, 6, 577-588.

Chisholm, B., Freeman, D., & Cooke, A. (2006). Identifying potential predictors of traumatic reactions to psychotic episodes. British Journal of Clinical Psychology, 45, 545-559.

Coleman, R. (1997). Recovery: An Alien Concept? (1st Edition). Gloucester, UK: Handsell Publishing.

Coleman, R. (1998). The politics of the madhouse. Gloucester,

UK: Handsell Publishing.

Coleman, R., & Smith, M. (2006). Working with voices: Victim to victor (2nd Edition). Fife, UK: P&P Press Ltd.

Coleman, R. & Taylor, K. (2007). Understanding recovery: Making recovery happen. A Working to Recovery training and education pack. Accessed online at: http://working torecovery.co.uk/products-page

Commission on Social Justice. (1994). Social justice: Strategies for national renewal. London: Institute for Public Policy Research.

Copeland, M. E. (1997). WRAP: Wellness Recovery Action Plan. Brattleboro, VT: Peach Press.

Corstens, D., Escher, S., & Romme, M. (2008). Accepting and working with voices: The Maastricht Approach. In A.Moskowitz, I. Schäfer, & M.J. Dorahy (Eds.), Psychosis, trauma and dissociation: Emerging perspectives on severe psychopathology (pp. 319–331). Oxford, UK: Wiley-Blackwell.

Curtis, L. C. (1997). New directions: International overview of best practices in recovery and rehabilitation for people with serious mental illness. A discussion paper prepared for the New Zealand Mental Health Commission. Burlington, VT: Center for Community Change.

Christmas, D. M. B., Curran, S., Matthews, K., & Eljamel, M. S. (2009). Neurosurgery for mental disorder, vagus nerve stimulation, and deep brain stimulation. Psychiatry, 8, 139-143.

Dencker, S. J., Lepp, M., & Malm, U. (1980). Do schizophrenics well adapted in the community need neuroleptics? A depot neuroleptic withdrawal study. Acta Psychiatrica Scandinavica, 61, 64-76.

Department of Health (DoH). (2003). Electroconvulsive

therapy: Survey covering the period from January 2002 to March 2002. London: Department of Health.

Fisher, D. B. (1994). Health care reform based on an empowerment model of recovery by people with psychiatric disabilities. Hospital and Community Psychiatry, 45, 913-915.

Fleischhacker, W. W., Meise, U., Günter, V., & Kurz, M. (1994). Compliance with antipsychotic drug treatment: Influence of side effects. Acta Psychiatrica Scandinavica, 89, 11-15.

Giles, J. (2002). Electroconvulsive therapy and the fear of deviance. Journal for the Theory of Social Behaviour, 32, 61-87.

Gitlin, M., Nuechterlein, K., Subotnik, K. L., Ventura, J., Mintz, J., Fogelson, D. L., Bartzokis, G., & Aravagiri, M. (2001). Clinical outcome following neuroleptic discontinuation in patients with remitted recent-onset schizophrenia. American Journal of Psychiatry, 158,1835-1842.

Glover, H. (2001). Developing recovery-orientated services for mental health services in England. London: National Institute for Mental Health.

Gracie, A., Freeman, D., Green, S., Garety, P. A., Kuipers, E., Hardy, A.Fowler, D. (2007). The association between traumatic experience, paranoia and hallucinations: A test of the predictions of psychological models. Acta Psychiatrica Scandinavica, 116, 280–289.

Greenfield, D. P. (2006). Organic approaches to the treatment of paraphilics and sex offenders. The Journal of Psychiatry and Law, 34, 437-445.

Haddock, G., Bentall, R. P., & Slade, P. D. (1996). Psychological treatment of auditory hallucinations:

Focusing or distraction? In G. Haddock & P. D. Slade (Eds.), Cognitive behavioural interventions with psychotic disorders (pp. 45-71). London: Routledge.

Hall, W. (2007). Harm-reduction guide to coming off psychiatric drugs: A publication by the Icarus Project and The Freedom Center. Accessed online at: http://theicarusproject.net/alternative-treatments/ harm-reduction-guide-to-coming-off-psychiatric-drugs

Harrow, M., & Jobe, T. H. (2007). Factors involved in outcome and recovery in schizophrenia patients not on antipsychotic medications: A 15-year multifollow-up study. Journal of Nervous and Mental Disorders, 195, 406-414.

Hartelius, H. (1952). Cerebral changes following electrically induced convulsions: An experimental study on cats. Acta Psychiatrica et Neurologica Scandinavica, 77, 1-28.

Hartmann, C. E. (2002). Life as death: Hope regained with ECT. Psychiatric Services, 53, 413-414.

Heinrichs, R. W. (2001). In search of madness: Schizophrenia and neuroscience. New York: Oxford University Press.

Hinsie, L. E., & Campbell, R. J. (1970). Psychiatric dictionary (4th Edition). Oxford, UK: Oxford University Press.

Hirsch, S. R., Gaind, R., Rohde, P. D., Stevens, B. C., & Wing, J. K. (1973). Outpatient maintenance of chronic schizophrenic patients with long-acting Fluphenazine: Double-blind placebo trial. British Medical Journal, 1, 633-637.

Hutton, P. (2010). What do Cochrane reviews say about the effectiveness of popular second-generation antipsychotics compared to placebo in treating schizophrenia? Paper presented at Giving Psychosis a Voice, Ipswich, UK, July 2010.

Institute of Psychiatry (2006). Risk of violence to other people. King's College, London: Institute of Psychiatry.

James, A. (2001). Raising our voices: An account of the Hearing Voices Movement. Gloucester, UK: Handsell Publishing.

Jaynes, J. (1976). The origin of consciousness in the breakdown of the bicameral mind. Boston: Houghton Mifflin.

Johnstone, L. (2000). Users and abusers of psychiatry (2nd Edition). London: Routledge.

Kim, M. C. & Lee, T. K. (2008). Stereotactic lesioning for mental illness. Acta Neurochirurgica Supplemetum, 101, 39-43.

Kinderman, P., & Bentall, R. P. (1996). Self-discrepancies and persecutory delusions: Evidence for a model of paranoid ideation. Journal of Abnormal Psychology, 105, 106-113.

Koopowitz, L. F., Chur-Hansen, A., Reid, S., & Blashki, M. (2003). The subjective experience of patients who received electroconvulsive therapy. Australian and New Zealand Journal of Psychiatry, 37, 49-54.

Large, M., Smith, G., Swinson, N., Shaw, J., & Nielssen, O. (2009). Homicide due to mental disorder in England and Wales over 50 years. British Journal of Psychiatry, 193, 130-133.

Lawson, W. (1994). Recovery: Implications of treatment of African Americans. Paper presented at The National Forum on Recovery for Persons with Severe Mental Illness, Columbus, OH.

LeFevre, S. J. (1996). Killing me softly: Self-harm, survival not suicide. Gloucester, UK: Handsell Publishing.

Lexchin, J. (1998). The relationship between pharmaceutical regulation and inappropriate prescribing: The case of psychotropic drugs in Canada during the 1960s and early 1970s. The International Journal of Risk and Safety in Medicine, 11, 49-59.

Liberman, R. P. (2002). Ten keys to recovery from schizophrenia. Accessed online at: http://baltimorecity.md.networkofcare.org/mh/library/detail.cfm?id=345&cat=40

Liberman, R. P., & Kopelowicz, A. (2002). Recovery from schizophrenia: A challenge for the 21st century. International Review of Psychiatry, 14, 245-255.

Liberman, R. P., Kopelowicz, A., Ventura, J., & Gutkind, D. (2002). Operational criteria and factors related to recovery from schizophrenia. International Review of Psychiatry, 14, 256-272.

Longden, E. (2010). Making sense of voices: A personal story of recovery. Psychosis: Psychological, Social and Integrative Approaches, 2, 255-259.

Metzl, J. M. (2003). Selling sanity through gender: The psychodynamics of psychotropic advertising. Journal of Medical Humanities, 1-2, 79-103.

Moniz, E. (1937/1994). Prefrontal leucotomy in the treatment of mental disorders. American Journal of Psychiatry, 151, 237-239.

Mosher, L. R., Gosden, R., & Beder, S. (2005). Drug companies and schizophrenia: Unbridled capitalism meets madness. In J. Read, L. R. Mosher, & R. P. Bentall (Eds.), Models of madness: Psychological, social and biological approaches to schizophrenia (pp. 115-130). Hove, UK: Routledge.

Murray, R. M. (2002). What do we need to treat in schizophrenia? Progress in Neurology and Psychiatry, 6, 20-23.

Offen, L., Waller, G., & Thomas, G. (2003). Is reported childhood sexual abuse associated with the psychopathological characteristics of patients who experience auditory hallucinations? Child Abuse and Neglect, 27, 919–927.

Parker, I., Georgaca, E., Harper, D., McLaughlin, T., & Stowell-Smith. (1995). Deconstructing psychopathology. London: Sage.

Pasamanick, B., Scarpitti, F. R., Lefton, M., Dinitz, S., Wernert, J. J., & McPheeters, H. (1964). Home vs. hospital care for schizophrenics. Journal of the American Medical Association, 187, 177-181.

Peele, S. (2005). Prescribed addiction. In J. A. Schaler (Ed.), Szasz under fire: The psychiatric abolitionist faces his critics (pp. 179-195). Peru, IL: Open Court.

Ragins, M. (2002). Road to recovery. Accessed online at: http://www.mhavillage.org/Web%20 Articles/6ARoadtoRecovery.pdf

Ragins, M. (2006). Person-centred vs. illness-centred. Accessed online at: http://www.ibhp.org/uploads/file/ Recovery%20 model%20paper-Ragins.pdf

Read, J. (2005). Electroconvulsive therapy. In J. Read, L. R. Mosher, & R. P. Bentall (Eds.), Models of madness: Psychological, social and biological approaches to schizophrenia (pp. 85-101). Hove, UK: Routledge.

Read, J., Agar, K., Argyle, N., & Aderhold, V. (2003). Sexual and physical abuse during childhood and adulthood as predictors of hallucinations, delusions and thought disorder. Psychology and Psychotherapy: Theory, Research, Practice, 76, 1–23.

Read, J., van Os, J., Morrison, A. P., & Ross, C. (2005). Childhood trauma, psychosis and schizophrenia: A literature review with theoretical and clinical implications. Acta Psychiatrica Scandinavica, 112, 330–350.

Reeves, A. (1997). Recovery: A holistic approach. Gloucester, UK: Handsell Publishing.

Reisner, A. D. (2003). The electroconvulsive therapy controversy: Evidence and ethics. Neuropsychology Review, 13, 199-219.

Romme, M. (2000). Redefining hearing voices. Based on a speech given at the launch of The Hearing Voices Network, Manchester, England, Summer 2000. Available online at: http://www.psychminded.co.uk/critical/marius.htm

Romme, M. (2010). Letter to the editor. Psychosis: Psychological, Social and Integrative Approaches, 2, 267-269.

Romme, M., & Escher, S. (1993). Accepting voices. London: Mind Publications,

Romme, M., & Escher, S. (2000). Making sense of voices. London: Mind Publications.

Romme, M., & Escher, S. (2010). Personal history and hearing voices. In F. Larøi & A. Aleman (Eds.), Hallucinations: A guide to treatment and management (pp. 233-257). Oxford: Oxford University Press.

Romme, M., Escher, S., Dillon, J., Corstens, D., & Morris, M. (Eds.), (2009). Living with voices: Fifty stories of recovery. Ross-on-Wye, UK: PCCS Books.

Rose, N. D. B. (1994). Essential psychiatry (2nd Edition). Oxford, UK: Wiley-Blackwell.

Shevlin, M., Dorahy, M., & Adamson, G. (2007). Childhood traumas and hallucinations: An analysis of the National Comorbidity Survey. Journal of Psychiatric Research, 41, 222-228.

Spaniol, L. (2001). Recovery from psychiatric disability: Implications for rehabilitation counseling education. Rehabilitation Education, 15, 167-175.

Special Hospital Service Authority (1993). Big, black and dangerous? London: Special Hospital Service Authority.

Sterling, P. (2000). ECT damage is easy to find if you look for it. Nature, 403, 242.

Tarrier, N., Beckett, R., Harwood, S., Baker, A., Yusupoff, L., Ugarteburu, I. (1993). A trial of two cognitive-behavioural methods of treating drug-resistant residual psychotic symptoms in schizophrenic patients: I. Outcome. British Journal of Psychiatry, 162, 524-532.

Taylor, P. J. & Gunn, J. (1999). Homicides by people with mental illness: Myth and reality. The British Journal of Psychiatry, 174, 9-14.

Templer, D. I., & Veleber, D. M. (1982). Can ECT permanently harm the brain? Clinical Neuropsychology, 4, 62-66.

Thomas, P. (1997). The dialectics of schizophrenia. London: Free Association Books.

Tone, A. (2008). The age of anxiety: A history of America's turbulent affair with tranquilizers. New York: Basic Books.

Trainor, J., Pomeroy, E., & Pape, B. (1993). A new framework for support: For people with serious mental health problems. Ontario: Canadian Mental Health Association.

UK ECT Review Group. (Carney, S. et al.). (2003). Efficacy and safety of ECT in depressive disorders. Lancet, 361, 799-808.

Warner, R. (2004). Recovery from schizophrenia: Psychiatry and political economy (3rd Edition). London: Routledge.

Watkins, J. (2006). Healing schizophrenia: Using medication wisely. Melbourne, AUS: Michelle Anderson Publishing.

Watkins, J. (2010). Unshrinking psychosis: Understanding and healing the wounded soul. Melbourne, AUS: Michelle Anderson Publishing.

Weiden, P. J. & Oltson, M. (1995). Cost of relapse in schizophrenia. Schizophrenia Bulletin, 21, 419-429.

Whitfield, C. L., Dube, S. R., Felitti, V. J., & Anda, R. F. (2005). Adverse childhood experiences and hallucinations. Child Abuse and Neglect, 29, 797–810.

Index

168